BUTTERFLY AND MOTH BOOK

Photograph by Lustig

And there was the Polyphemus in apple-pie order

BUTTERFLY AND MOTH BOOK

PERSONAL STUDIES AND OBSERVATIONS OF THE MORE
FAMILIAR SPECIES

BY

ELLEN ROBERTSON-MILLER

WITH ILLUSTRATIONS FROM DRAWINGS BY THE AUTHOR AND
PHOTOGRAPHS BY J. LYONEL KING, G. A. BASH,
DR. F. D. SNYDER AND OTHERS

NEW YORK
CHARLES SCRIBNER'S SONS
1926

TO MY HUSBAND

AND THE TWO GOOD FRIENDS, J. N. M. AND L. W. G.,
WHO HAVE ALWAYS ENCOURAGED AND AIDED
ME IN MY WORK WITH INSECTS
THIS BOOK IS DEDICATED

FOREWORD

My interest in Moths and Butterflies was awakened some ten years ago while at the farm on which we spent our summers.

The big flower garden and the old orchard served free luncheons to these insects and, judging by numbers, they appreciated the treats offered.

At the time I was in need of an entire change of thought— a relaxation from the strain which had come with the long illness of the little mother. She had grown better, but I realized that henceforth she would always require my personal care and attention, and I wanted to give her not only these but some new interests which might replace in part other interests that she would be obliged to relinquish.

It was then that the Moths and Butterflies solved these problems, for they led us into the fairy-land of Natural Science, where, as we journeyed, we forgot much of the fatigue and pain of earlier days.

The following year I found that the children of the neighborhood, and even the children's parents, were taking an interest in the insects which we reared in soap-box vivariums on the side porch, for they began to bring and send us specimens found in their gardens and fields, and were always glad to learn about the life-histories under observation. Of course, this interest pleased me, and I began to ask the little folks to the house when something especially important was to take place, like the hatching of moth eggs, the moulting of a family of caterpillars, or the spinning of cocoons. On one such occasion, as a group of boys and girls watched a small white butterfly emerge from its chrysalis and heard me explain that the week before the butterfly had been a green "cabbage worm," a lad looked up and asked: "Why don't you write about these things and tell other children what you tell us?" It was a new idea, but the idea remained, and the tiny seed sowed by the boy germinated and took root. I did begin to write about the insects as I knew them—and now I have gathered together some of those first stories published in different periodicals and have added others of more recent date and am sending them out in book form, with the hope that they will lessen the antipathy which many persons feel for creeping things and aid others to gain a more intimate acquaintance with the "frail children of the air." But, most of all, I want this book to reach some one weary and over-taxed, and help him to find the rest, relaxation, and enjoyment in the fairy-land of Natural Science that the little mother and I found when the Moths and Butterflies showed us the way.

I wish to express my thanks to "Country Life in America," the Presbyterian Board of Publication, "The American Inventor," "The New Idea Magazine," "Brooklyn Eagle," "Philadelphia North American," "Our Animal Friends," and the "Nature Story Syndicate" for certain illustrations and extracts of subject-matter used in this book; also to acknowledge with deep appreciation the services and kindly interest of the many friends who have aided me in my work.

E. R.-M.

CONTENTS

CONTENTS

ILLUSTRATIONS

ILLUSTRATIONS

ILLUSTRATIONS

ILLUSTRATIONS

ILLUSTRATIONS

ILLUSTRATIONS

xvi

ILLUSTRATIONS

ILLUSTRATIONS

INITIALS AND TAILPIECES FROM PHOTOGRAPHS AND DRAWINGS BY
THE AUTHOR.

COVER DESIGN BY MAY AMES.

BUTTERFLY AND MOTH BOOK

BUTTERFLY AND MOTH BOOK

CHAPTER I

THE MOTH AND THE BUTTERFLY

"In Nature's infinite book of secrecy
A little I can read."

THE history of a moth or butterfly is a veritable fairy tale, and of absorbing interest when we study the development of the insect through the four periods of its existence. The first period is that of the egg laid by a moth or butterfly mother; the second, that of the larva or caterpillar which hatches from it; the third, the mysterious pupa state into which the caterpillar passes after it has eaten its fill of green leaves and is fully grown. In the fourth period the remarkable transformation is completed, the insect comes from the pupa shell a beautiful creature like its parents, with wonderful colors and designs upon the wings. These patterns are due to minute scales, and on account of them the moths and butterflies are classed among insects as the Lepidoptera or Scale-wings.

To the naked eye, the scales seem but so much dust; under the microscope, however, they show great variation in shape and size. They are arranged with overlapping edges like the scales of a fish, and, as we who have captured butterflies know, the slightest touch loosens them.

1

A frequent question is: "How can I tell a moth from a butterfly?" Usually by the feelers or antennæ located on the head—those of a butterfly being always thread-like and clubbed

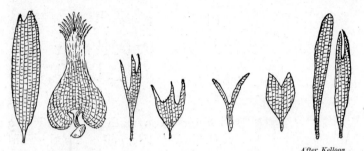

After Kellogg

Scales of moths and butterflies, showing some of the variations in shape and size
(greatly enlarged)

at the end, while those of moths vary according to species and are of several different patterns. Another difference is that the majority of moths fly at night and the butterflies in the

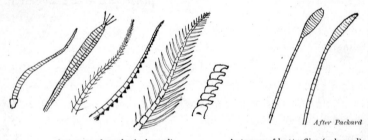

After Packard

Antennæ of moths (enlarged)   Antennæ of butterflies (enlarged)

daytime; and again, the moths rest with wings held horizontally, in roof form, or wrapped about the body, while butterflies when at rest usually hold their wings in a vertical position.

THE MOTH AND THE BUTTERFLY

We know that the butterflies go to the flowers and to the sap of trees for their food, sipping the nectar through long hollow tongues. When not in use, these tongues are coiled like a watch-spring and held close to the mouth between a pair of feathery mufflers, the palpi of the insect.

Certain varieties of moths also have tongues through which they feed, but other species, that of the *Saturniidæ*, for example, lack this organ or have it but poorly developed, therefore they cannot eat.

Another question frequently asked is: "How long does a moth or butterfly live?" We can readily understand that these silk-spinning *Saturniidæ* with undeveloped mouth-parts will have but a brief winged existence. But a number of our common butterflies pass the winter in a dormant condition.

Photograph by King

Position of butterfly at rest

They cling to the under surfaces of boards and twigs or hide in the crevices of old buildings or among leaves. We all know them, for it is they who go careening and frolicking before us in the sunshine as we take our first spring walks. Other butterflies and many moths only live through the summer, or until their food supply is exhausted or some accident overtakes them.

The eggs of moths and butterflies vary in size, shape, and color according to species. Some are the merest specks, while others are more than one-sixteenth of an inch in diameter.

3

They are spherical, flattened, oval, and of other forms, and may be white or of a pale blue, green, violet, yellow, or red color. When examined under a lens, many are found to be exquisitely carved and ornamented. These eggs are laid by the moth or butterfly singly, in groups, chains, en masse, or

Photograph by King

Position of moth at rest (two-thirds life size)

so as to form a ring about some twig; but whatever the manner of ovipositing, they are, with rare exceptions, placed on or near such plants as will be acceptable to the wee crawlers when they emerge. This strange instinct of the winged mother in caring for her caterpillar children has caused much discussion among scientists. Some entomologists hold that the adult insect remembers the food which nourished it in its larva state; others think that the food plant is sought instinctively

4

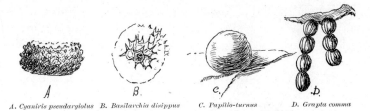

A. *Cyaniris pseudargiolus* B. *Basilarchia disippus* C. *Papilio-turnus* D. *Grapta comma*

Eggs of butterflies (greatly enlarged)

and located through the sense of smell.   Be this as it may, we know that the Monarch selects milkweed, the Violet-tip hop, and the little white butterflies, so numerous about the puddles of muddy roads, cabbage or nasturtium leaves as nurseries for their young, and that these same young, like all caterpillars, refuse to eat any but their natural food plant.

It is sometimes difficult to secure fresh leaves of a certain kind for a family of growing larvæ, or to feed a caterpillar which has come to you with nothing to indicate what it has lived upon. I frequently try different plants in the hope that I may chance upon a satisfactory substitute for what is desired, but I am seldom successful. Still my efforts have sometimes been rewarded, as in the case of the green "worm" which I found hiding in a rolled leaf whose edges it had cleverly stitched together.   The leaf belonged to a small seedling plum tree, and I removed it and the occupant together with extra food leaves to a glass jar.   Three days later, I was surprised to see that the caterpillar was not eating.   Something was wrong, but what I could not tell.   Two more days passed, and it had shrivelled to half its former size, but still it refused to eat the plum-tree leaves. An inspiration came to me. Did the larva use the plum tree for rest and concealment and feed on something else? I gathered leaves from trees and shrubs in the neighborhood and placed his wormship in their midst, but he would none of them.

The only plants within easy reach were clover and grass, so these were tried. The clover was encountered first, and I thought the larva was going to take a bite, because it sniffed at the weed for a time, but finally passed on and came to the grass. Then what a change! The green "worm" had found its own, and it ate, and it ate, and it ate, and then it rested, and I could just feel the silent contentment that radiated from its swelling body.

The log house of a caterpillar

To me there is no time in the life of the lepidopterous insects when they are so interesting as during their creeping days. If we can overcome our dislike for crawling things sufficiently to study them in this state we shall learn how clever they are and how wonderfully they construct their homes. Like little artisans they excavate in the ground, work in wood, make log houses, cut and sew leaves into tents, spin fine silk, and build suspension bridges over which they pass and repass.

Every caterpillar has a head and a body with twelve segments. On the three segments at the back of the head are to be found the six true feet, and usually there are fleshy prolegs on the sixth, seventh, eighth, ninth, and twelfth segments. All or part of the prolegs are wanting in certain species, but the true legs are always present. If we remember this, it is not difficult to distinguish a caterpillar from the young of saw-flies, beetles, and from the true worms, centipedes and such.

A caterpillar breathes through openings called spiracles along the sides of its body. Its one duty in life is to eat, therefore it

A caterpillar

grows rapidly and soon finds that its skin is uncomfortably tight and must be discarded. In order to do this it first expels all surplus liquids from its body; then, with scarcely an exception, it spins some form of a silken carpet with fine threads drawn from a little spinneret below its mouth, and into this it fastens its feet and begins to squirm and wriggle until it bursts open the old skin, from which it crawls forth in the glory of new clothes.

As soon as a larva is fully matured it prepares for the great

Photograph by Lustig

A Swallow-tail larva ready to become a chrysalis and
supported by the silk rope (twice life size)

change through which it must pass ere it becomes a winged
adult. If the caterpillar is that of a butterfly, it weaves a little
rosette of silk on some convenient surface and into this catches
its last pair of prolegs, then, if it be a Swallow-tail, a Cabbage-
worm, or a larva of their kind, it spins a fine rope of silk and so
attaches this that a loop is formed through which the insect
pushes a part of its body and thus rests in safety while the last
caterpillar skin is being pushed off from the pupa or chrysalis

8

beneath. On the other hand, the butterfly larva may be one that does not feel the need of the girth; if so, it attaches its last pair of prolegs in the silken button and swings off into space head down, and in this position awaits the chrysalis.

The legs, long tongue, and folded wings show through the pupa covering

Each newly arrived chrysalis performs a clever athletic feat. Just as the larva skin is to be discarded, it reaches for and finds the rosette of silk and into it fastens the hooks on the cremaster, at the tail end of the body. At first the chrysalis is soft and easily damaged, but soon a liquid is exuded over its surface, and this hardens so that the pupa is protected by a shell. The legs, long tongue, folded wings, and segmented body can be easily seen through this covering.

There is a tendency toward protective coloration in butterfly chrysalides; those adhering to old wood are quite apt to be of a gray-brown tone, while others attached to or among leaves will have a greenish color. Scientists have been trying to find out what causes this variation. For a time it was quite universally believed that it was due to the photographic action of light on the moist pupa skin, but Prof. E.

The pupa is protected by a shell

B. Poulton, of Oxford, England, has disproved this theory and advances another; namely, that the larva, after it has ceased to eat, is influenced by its surroundings during the twenty hours which precede the last twelve hours of its caterpillar existence. He also finds that certain colors have no influence upon the larva, and that many larvæ seem unconscious of their surroundings.

Vanessa antiopa butterfly clinging to the chrysalis from which it recently emerged. The lifted "trap-door" shows the opening through which it escaped (twice life size)

If an insect does not pass the winter in the chrysalis period, it will, in from one to four weeks, come forth as a butterfly. That section of the chrysalis covering the legs, tongue, and antennæ is first pushed up like a trap-door, and these members, one by one, appear and are followed by the damp body of the fly, whose wings are caught up in little rosettes at the sides of the thorax. The insect clings for a time to a near-by support, and gradually the wings are unfurled and air from the body cavity pumped into their veins. If, by any chance, however, these have been injured, the butterfly will be obliged to go through the remainder of its life on crumpled wings, but if all is well, it will in a few hours be ready to go out into the world,

10

find its mate, and reproduce its kind. The caterpillars of moths as well as those of butterflies undergo this strange transformation, but usually within closed doors. The Tomato worm and all of its family go into the ground before pupating, while certain larvæ secure suitable resting-places by tunnelling into old wood; others, like those of the silk-moths, spin a variety of cocoons. But whatever the form, each tomblike structure holds the insect till it is summoned forth, a fairy creature, winged and beautiful.

CHAPTER II

THE SECRET OF THE SILKEN POCKETS

The Promethea, *Callosamia promethea*

> "Dead hangs the crysalis amid
>   Its bower of living green.
> Dead? No! It bursts! and issuing forth
>   An insect form is seen.
> O marvel! that the grave of life
>   A living thing should yean!"

THE winter homes of some of our insects are wonderfully made little snuggeries. To me, perhaps the most interesting are the cocoon cradles of the silk-moths.

At any time during late fall and winter one may see several varieties of these small silken pockets attached to the denuded twigs. During these seasons I rarely return from a walk in the suburbs empty-handed. Still it is April before I go forth purposely to hunt cocoons. Then what a pleasure it is to get out-of-doors and tramp among the fragrant wetness of stirring things! How beautiful are the red stems of the osier dogwood against the gray misty background of meadow and wood! How we like to pick them and the twigs of the golden willow, and, best of all, the first "pussies" as they peep out in their furry coats! Besides there are the cocoons, each holding its promise of a "spring opening" when a "winged flower" will step forth arrayed as was Solomon in all his glory.

One day, while passing through an open wood in which there was a growth of wild cherry, I noticed a number of these pockets swinging from the twigs. Examination showed that each was spun within a partly curled leaf, whose petiole had been strengthened, and then fastened to the parent twig by silken threads. So cleverly was the work done that it was impossible to detach the spec-

Photograph by King
A moth clinging to a cocoon from which she has just emerged (two-thirds life size)

imens, so I broke off the twigs holding them and carried these home, for I had found the cocoons of the Promethea silk-moth. I kept a close watch upon the queer little cradles, and on the first of June discovered a moth clinging to the lower end of the one from which she had just emerged. Her damp wings were still crumpled, but they at once began to strengthen and take form, so that within a few minutes the insect was full-fledged and of a dull reddish hue. All of the characteristic bands and markings of the species became apparent, even to the snakelike heads depicted upon the tips of the fore wings, a device which, under certain conditions, is thought to protect the Promethea from the attacks of birds.

Photograph by King
As the wings begin to strengthen and take form (two-thirds life size)

These wings were limp, however, and it was several hours before they were sufficiently firm to be of service. During this time the Promethea waved them frequently, in order to dry the parti-colored scales upon their surface.

About four o'clock I was surprised to find that the outside of the window screen, near which the cocoon hung, was literally alive with moths similar to, but of a much darker color than, the one that had emerged at noon. How did it happen that they were there? I had learned that one of the distinguishing features between moths and butterflies is that the former, with few exceptions, fly at night, while the latter are on the wing during the day. I concluded, and rightly, that the Promethea was an exception to the rule. But why had the moths collected, and in such numbers, on the outside

14

Photograph by King

All of the characteristic bands and markings of the species became
apparent (two-thirds life size)

of the screen? Simply because they were males who "would
a-wooing go." They had scented "my lady" from afar and
had come to visit her, but the screen was a barrier through
which they could not pass; they did not realize this, however,
or possibly ignored the fact, for they continued to batter their
wings against the wires until I hung the cocoon and the female
in the yard; then the entire number fluttered hither and thither,

Photograph by King

Female moth clinging to her cocoon, and a male visitor
(two-thirds life size)

until they again located the moth, which, after a deal of co·
quetting, chose a very ragged gallant as her mate.

She began to lay her eggs that night, and she continued to
deposit them for the next three days. They were possibly as
large as the head of a small pin, of a pinkish white, but much
stained with the dark secretion that fastened them to the leaves
and twigs of the young wild cherry. Gradually the large
body of the moth grew smaller and smaller, and her strength

16

became less and less, until, no longer able to cling to a support, she dropped to the ground exhausted; her brief life upon the wing was finished.

Twelve days later the tiny caterpillars began to emerge from their egg-shells. There were over two hundred of them, and they cuddled close together in groups on the under side of the leaves, where they fed side by side. Their yellow and black striped coats made them quite conspicuous. In about ten days some of the wee crawlers stopped eating, grew dull in color, and became very dumpish. The following afternoon I found several had moulted and were eagerly feeding. They looked very bright and fresh among the other larvæ, and as I stood wondering just how the change of dress had been accomplished, a caterpillar decided to make its toilet, apparently for my benefit.

It shook a kind of mask from off its face, the skin back of the head split open, then, with many contortions, the larva crawled slowly out. First one leg and then another was withdrawn until the entire body was freed from the outgrown covering.

When the Prometheas moulted a second time their color and markings were very different, and they continued to alter their appearance with each succeeding moult, the fifth and last skin being a blue-green in tone,

Promethea larvæ after the second moult
(two-thirds life size)

ornamented with what might be compared to black buttons in button-holes of blue. Near the head there were four brilliant red tubercles and a yellow one at the rear or caudal end

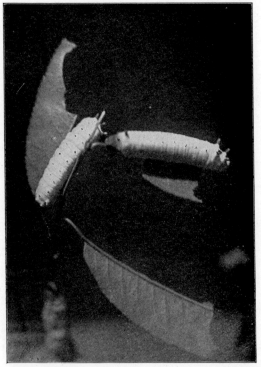

Photograph by King

Promethea larvæ in their last skins (two-thirds life size)

of the body. The larvæ no longer lived together as they had done when young, their gay appearance making this unnecessary, for not only the lower animals but man senses danger when he encounters a vivid color combination in nature, such is the Prometheas possess. And while such a device is misleading in some cases, it so frequently signals poison, bad taste, or bad odor, that instinctively we heed the warning.

The Prometheas are shy caterpillars. I never saw them quarrelling among themselves, and if you disturb one it does not hiss or spit out undigested food at you, neither will it threaten you with its uplifted or swaying body, as do many of the larvæ, but, instead, it will draw its head farther beneath its thoracic segments and cling close to the leaf upon which it rests with a kind of mute appeal to be left alone.

Then when its creeping days are about over, it begins to prepare for winter by spinning a warm little dwelling in which to pass the cold weather. And as it works it shows a remarkable instinct, for it weaves not only the cocoon, but the silken threads which attach it to the tree. How does the insect know that in nature the leaves fall, and that the one holding its home must be strengthened if it is to escape the fate of its fellows?

CHAPTER III

A HOME NOT MADE WITH HANDS

The Cecropia, *Samia cecropia*

"And there's never a blade nor a leaf too mean
To be some happy creature's palace."

IT is unnecessary to go to the country or even to the suburbs for certain species of cocoons. I frequently find those of *Samia cecropia* upon the trees and shrubs in our dooryards, and especially upon the maples that shade so many of our residence streets, while I have secured more than one fine specimen on a weed stalk, close to the ground.

These cocoons are pouches of rough brownish silk, frequently bedecked with bits of dried leaves, and one can usually tell if a cocoon holds a living insect by slightly shaking it. If it does, the motion will cause the pupa to roll within its silken wrappings. Sometimes, however, a specimen, secured after a deal of trouble, is found to be parasitized, or possibly empty, punctured by the beak of a bird, for the Cecropia architects are not always able to provide against this calamity although they build with reference to it. If we drop an *empty* cocoon into boiling water and then cut it open crosswise, we shall see for ourselves what methods the insects employ, how they spin a room with padded walls about a smaller room, and also how they conceal the door-way.

Cocoons gathered in winter should be kept in a cool room, otherwise the artificial heat of the house will awaken the moths before Dame Nature has the leaf luncheons ready for their children. When such a misfortune occurs, the moth mother cannot delay her work of egg-laying as do certain butterflies, for, belonging to the family *Saturniidæ*, she is unable to eat, and will therefore live but a short time, possibly fourteen days.

As a rule, moths and butterflies select with seeming care a plant that will nourish their young, and on this they deposit their eggs. But the Cecropia, even under favorable conditions, is not al-

Photograph by Snyder

These cocoons are pouches of rough brownish silk

ways a careful mother, for I have found her eggs upon a gatepost and even upon a stone. Larvæ thus stranded are able, no doubt, to reach one of their several food plants, for these

Photograph by King

After casting their first skins

crawlers are willing to feed upon the leaves of grape, goose-berry, maple, wild cherry, willow, and other trees and shrubs, with seemingly no preference for any one of them.

The oval eggs, a trifle larger than those of Promethea, are attached to the surface upon which they are laid with a se-cretion which discolors them, but when freed from this glue, they appear white until just before hatching; then the black skin of the imprisoned caterpillar shows through. The lar-væ emerge in from fifteen to eighteen days, and while I have never been so fortunate as to see them leave their shells, I have found them when less than an hour old, and they were always black.

Once I watched a brood during its several moults and dis-covered that, after casting its first skin, a larva appeared with a brown body and a horn-colored head and tubercles, but that in twenty minutes this color disappeared, leaving the caterpillar as black as it had been before. With the second moult a permanent change in the color of the body became apparent; it was now of a dull orange with rows of black tubercles. After the third moult the larva showed red tubercles on its thoracic segments and a green head with black markings, and with the fourth and last moult the entire body became green, while the red tubercles changed to orange, the black ones along the back to yellow, and those on the sides to blue.

The brilliant colors of the Cecropia during its last creeping days together with its large size make it a conspicuous caterpillar, and it feeds on so many common trees and plants that it is very well known.

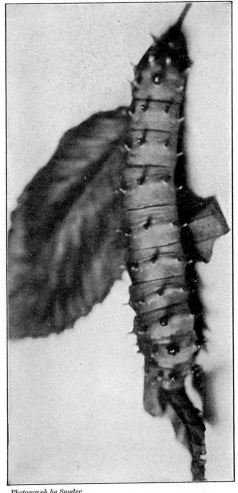

Photograph by Snyder

The Cecropia during its last creeping days is a conspicuous caterpillar

One brood which I had under observation fed for ten days after their last moult, and then began to spin their cocoons. The silk as it came from the spinnerets was creamy-white, and when a cocoon was but partly finished it suggested a delicate lace mantle through whose meshes the gorgeous colors of the caterpillar showed dimly. Hours after a larva was no longer visible I could hear it smoothing and shaping the interior walls of its winter home; but when silence reigned I knew that it had dis-

Photograph by King

Cecropia moths when they waken find an open doorway at the end of their cocoons

robed for the last time and become, not a freshly dressed caterpillar, but a mummy-like chrysalis.

A HOME NOT MADE WITH HANDS

The Cecropia moths when they waken find at the end of their cocoons an open door-way slightly veiled with loose silken threads which the insects brush to one side as they emerge.

The moths have brown wings bordered with tan and crossed

The body of the moth is large

by bands of red and white; in each there is a light crescent edged with black, and a very good representation of an open eye stares at you from the tip of each fore wing, which is shaped so that it somewhat resembles a snake's head, a device that may protect the insect from certain of its bird enemies. The body of the moth is large and, with one exception, I have always found it ringed with dull red and white. The exception, which probably proves the rule, was a female that emerged from a cocoon spun by a caterpillar that had been reared by a boy friend. This moth had a body banded with black and white. Her eggs did not hatch, so I was unable to learn whether her unusual markings would have been transmitted to her children.

CHAPTER IV

A CATERPILLAR THAT MAY SOME DAY GIVE US CHEAP AND DURABLE SILK

The Cynthia, *Philosamia cynthia*

"More servants wait on man
    Than he'll take note of. In every path
    He treads down that which doth befriend him."

THE Cynthia caterpillars, bedecked in "powder and patches," were on a young tree of heaven, an ailantus, in Prospect Park, Brooklyn, and oh, the thrill of delight which passed over me when I saw them for the first time! They were of all ages, and not only were there larvæ on the tree, but also freshly spun cocoons, and, best of all, several eggs, which seemed unusually small for the size of the mature insect.

Do you wonder that I was excited? My home is in the Middle West, and these Cynthias are common only in the Atlantic States. They are foreigners, Chinese cousins, we might say, of our native silk-moths.

I noticed that the crawlers fed on the under side of the leaves; they were shy, and when disturbed would hunch themselves much as do the Prometheas.

The youngest members of the family, not having acquired the habit of powdering, showed yellow-green bodies dotted with black, and black heads, while on specimens two or more inches in length the powder—a waxy bloom—was very pronounced, giving a creamy appearance to the insect and obscuring somewhat its cerulean blue tubercles.

Upon removing the captured caterpillars from my collecting-box, I discovered that this powder came off easily, and later it occurred to me that it might be responsible for the truly pleasing odor of the larvæ.

On the following day, a partly grown Cynthia spun considerable silk on the upper surface of a leaf and clung to this while it jerked the front portion of its body from side to side spasmodically. As a result of these gymnastics, the old skin burst open and was quickly discarded—a performance that enlivened my homeward journey and proved interesting to a number of my fellow-travellers.

While packing for the trip West, I had found that three of the larvæ were ready to make their cocoons, so placed them in a box by themselves; but as I had more packages than I could manage, at the last moment I divided their box and gave one-half of it to an earth-burrowing larva already seeking seclusion in the dirt of its tin can. En route the partition wall gave way, and I discovered caterpillars, dirt, and silken threads in a confused and wriggling mix-up. The amount of silk which the Cynthias had spun, however, indicated a determination on their part to make cocoons in spite of their strange room-mate and unnatural surroundings; it also showed that they had worked most diligently, for on the lid of the box there was a piece of dense cloth amounting to six square inches, and this was only part of what they had accomplished.

These caterpillars lived for five days after I reached home, but apparently they had used up their supply of silk, for they showed no inclination to continue weaving. Their bodies contracted until they were like balls, and I hoped that the insects would change to the pupa form without the protection of silken cases, but in this I was disappointed.

Others of the family spun cocoons in due time, however,

The Cynthia caterpillars were on a young tree of heaven (two-thirds life size)

and like those found in Prospect Park, each was made in a leaflet of the long compound leaf of the ailantus. They were similar to the cocoons of the Promethea, although they were not so dense nor were they so carefully attached to the twig.

I left these cocoons in the breeding-cage or vivarium where the larvæ had lived, and on the twenty-fourth of the next July a perfect female emerged. I placed her with a bottle of ailantus in an empty vivarium, and she at once flew to a twig and there hung quietly all day.

The patterns and tones on the wings of moths and butterflies are so varied and beautiful that they are a never-ending source of delight to me, and here was a "first view." I sat down before Miss Cynthia and by degrees familiarized myself with the details of her exquisite coloring.

The ground tone of the wings was brown, such a soft brown, with the merest suggestion of yellow dusted over them, as if the moth, while passing some pollen-laden blossom, had been sprinkled with the golden grains. The wings were crossed by a dull lavender band whose outer edge was lost in lace-like frost-work. This lavender color was also to be seen on the tips of the fore wings around the eye-spots, but the accentuated color note of the moth, near the middle of each wing, was a yellow crescent with a transparent border above.

For eight days Miss Cynthia remained practically in one position, and I hoped that her presence and the odor of green food upon which the caterpillars feed would arouse some gallant sleeping over-late within his snug retreat. But she must have grown weary of waiting, for after laying a few eggs she died on the morning of August the third. Then, on the afternoon of that very day, out came a male, which was the last moth to emerge from my cocoons, the others having been parasitized. His markings seemed identical with those of the

Male moth and cocoon (two-thirds life size)

female, but the tips of the fore wings were more sharply curved, and the brown portions had assumed a shade of olive.

If only he had not been such a laggard, I might have reared an entire family of these foreign caterpillars upon the big ailantus tree in my garden, and experimented with their cocoons. Thus far no cheap and practical way of reeling them has been discovered, but when this problem is solved, the Cynthias—first imported into Europe and then into America with the hope that they might prove of economic value—may yield us a coarse grade of durable silk.

CHAPTER V

LADY LUNA

Actias luna

"Winged flowers, or flying gems."

THE little mother in her wheel-chair used to sit on the side porch while I fed the caterpillars. I think it was because so many former pleasures and occupations were at the time denied her that she became interested—as I had hoped she would—in my study of moths and butterflies.

This side porch had been converted by degrees into an insect nursery. Breeding-cages, jars of "worms," boxes of chrysalides, and the like were to be seen everywhere. However, it was a pleasant, shady corner on a warm morning—so pleasant and peaceful that sometimes the little invalid would doze and dream. One day when I returned from a long search after milkweed for the Monarch caterpillars, I was not surprised to find her sleeping.

But what did she have in her hand? A great green moth whose body was quivering from fear. Poor frightened insect, it could not understand how soft and gentle was the hand that held it. I removed the specimen, and as I did so little mother looked up and said, "Oh, did I fall asleep?"

"Yes," I replied, "and while you slept a moth flew right down into your hand."

"Oh, no, you are mistaken; a little boy brought it for the 'bug-woman.'"

"And you allowed a boy to call your only daughter a 'bug-woman,' did you?"

"Well," she said, looking around her, "it seems to me that you deserve the name, as long as you raise these things. But what about the moth?"

"Let us examine it. It is *Actias luna;* Luna, because it has these transparent eye-spots, one in the centre of each wing, and

Photograph by King

This side porch had been converted by degrees into an insect nursery

do you see how they are outlined in white, black, and yellow? Notice this purple border on the front wings and over the thorax; is it not a beautiful contrast to the delicate green of the insect?"

"Yes, but the body is not green," interrupted the little woman, and she began to stroke its soft white "fur," an act

34

that possibly soothed the moth, for it soon became quiet and rested with horizontal wings. This position showed to good advantage the long tails, which I discovered were slightly frilled on one side. I knew the specimen was a female because the feathered antennæ or feelers were narrow and the abdomen heavy with eggs. So I placed the moth in a shoe-box where she might oviposit in comfort.

We called her "Lady Luna," and we thought the name appropriate, for she was most beautiful to look upon, and, moreover, as she was a silk-worm moth—with mouth-parts undeveloped—she did not eat and consequently could not work.

When night came, and she had shown no disposition to lay her eggs, I concluded that she was but recently emerged from her chrysalis and was still unmated. Having read that a male Luna will seek and locate a female, even though she is in the heart of a great city, I decided to fasten "Lady Luna" to a twig in an apple tree; this I did with a piece of soft grass tied about her thorax.

In the morning when I went for her I was greatly surprised, as I reached up among the leaves, to see a Luna similar to my first specimen, but smaller, flutter to the ground and there remain perfectly still. No, it was not "my lady," for she was where I had placed her the evening before. This, then, was the gallant, who had come a-courting and remained too late. In attire he was quite as exquisite as his bride, only the white "fur" of his body showed a yellow tinge, as did also the green of his wings. He was a perfect specimen, and as I had been trying for two years to find one of his kind, I secured him for my collection.

I then returned the female to her shoe-box, and that evening, the twenty-sixth of May, she began to deposit her white eggs, gluing them by means of a brown liquid to the sides of the box.

Three days later I set her free, for she had already laid over two hundred eggs, a number quite sufficient for my purpose. These I knew would not hatch under twelve or fourteen days,

Photograph by King

Actias luna moth (two-thirds life size)

so I labelled the box containing them and placed it on a convenient shelf.

Early in the morning of the thirteenth day, I examined the eggs, but no larvæ had appeared. As the weather was fine and the little woman needed an outing, we went down the road to where a great willow overhangs the brook, and on this tree found, as I was certain that we would, the caterpillars of two common butterflies. We became so interested in securing these that it was noon before we returned to the house.

As I wheeled the chair on to the porch from the "incline," I glanced at the Luna's box, and behold! wee yellow-green larvæ not only were crawling over its sides, but some were moving rapidly on the wall of the porch toward the woodbine.

What directed their course? Did they seek the vine intentionally, and if so, was it because of an inherited instinct, which made its odor suggest food and shelter?

A fully grown caterpillar

The family dinner that day was delayed, for I was afraid that, unless the young caterpillars were at once fed, they might die, and since none of their food trees, such as walnut, butternut, hickory, and oak, grew in our yard, "the man with the wheel" went to the park and brought back fresh walnut leaves for their benefit. The ungrateful little creatures, however, would have none of these, although I had read that walnut was their favorite food plant. When evening came, I was quite certain that I should fail to rear "Lady Luna's" children. But in the morning I found that all of the caterpillars that had hatched, some two hundred and ten, were industriously feeding upon the leaves.

From this time on they gave us little trouble until they were a month old. Then a sickness appeared among them. If a larva was attacked it would show black spots and become limp and lifeless. The disease seemed highly contagious, so I separated the family into several groups, and also freed a number of the insects, hoping that instinct would lead these to one of nature's remedies; but, so far as I know, none of the affected members survived.

The caterpillars, when fully grown, had pea-green heads and clear green bodies that were somewhat darker beneath. At the back edge of each abdominal segment there was a yellow line, and one of the same conspicuous color extended on either side of the body below the spiracles. The tubercles were red or rose and out of each grew fine light hairs.

On account of sickness and unavoidable accidents, only fifty-nine of these caterpillars matured and spun their cocoons.

Some of the insects grew much more rapidly than did others; in fact, there was one that expelled the liquid from its body on

The cocoon of the first spinner

July the ninth. Soon after this it became a faded yellow color and crawled down into the dry leaves at the bottom of the breeding-cage. Here I noticed that it drew a leaf over its body and fastened it with silk threads. Back and forth like a shuttle went the head, each time adding a strand to the web; and during the operation the larva reversed its position and shaped the cocoon until it was satisfactory.

The last Luna disappeared into what I supposed would be its winter quarters sixty days after the mother moth deposited

The pupa stood upon its caudal extremity

her first egg; fifty-one days after, the first larva appeared; and twenty days after, the first cocoon was formed.

Then "the man with the wheel" said, "Oh! but I am glad this is over," and I sympathized with him, for there had been days when, on account of the leaves withering from heat, two trips to the walnut tree had been necessary.

We found that the pupæ of the Luna were very noisy. Many a time the little mother called me to see if the moths were hatching. Once, out of curiosity, I opened a cocoon to find, if I might, why the inmate was so restless. The pupa stood upon its caudal extremity and seemed to bow and scrape; the face mask peered out from between the wing coverings, as I have seen the face of an old woman look at me from the folds of her shawl. It was actually uncanny and made me think of a mummy reanimated, but so wrapped and bound that it could only plead mutely for its deliverance.

In our locality the Luna is supposed to be single-brooded, so we were greatly surprised to find three large moths on August the sixth in the breeding-cage where the cocoons were kept, and, strange to say, none of these were from the cocoon of the first spinner.

For fifteen days the insects continued to emerge, and the little mother and I spent a good deal of time watching them. After moistening the threads at the end of the cocoon, one would push forth its antennæ, then a leg, and at length it would step out as smartly as a lady leaving her carriage. The wings with the "tails" folded were looped up, and the moth would walk rapidly, trailing its long white body over dirt, leaves, and cocoons, with no seeming injury either to it or the delicate draperies. In a few hours it would gain strength and firmness and hang like a winged flower, seeming to realize that it was a thing of beauty.

The Lunas were very quiet during this period of their lives and showed none of the vivacity so characteristic of the common silk-moth, Promethea. Several males came about the porch and were captured and placed in the breeding-cage, for I wanted to raise another family that I might have some winter cocoons for exchange. In this I was disappointed, for out of the large number of eggs laid by the daughters of "Lady Luna," not one hatched. Possibly some ichneumon fly had appropriated them as nurseries and supply houses for her progeny. However, as one of the cocoons remained unopened, I hoped that its occupant would prove to be a female. During the winter, I often heard the pupa turning in its bed, and, as June approached, I supposed that I was guarding the specimen with due care, but one day I examined it only to find the house empty and the inmate gone.

Photograph by King

CHAPTER VI

OUR COMMON SILK-WORM

THE POLYPHEMUS, *Telea polyphemus*

"Every worm beneath the sun
Draws different threads,
And late or soon, spins toiling out
Its own cocoon."

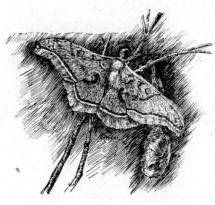

THE Polyphemus cocoon is very different from that of the Cecropia, not only in the way it is made but also in the way it is attached to the tree. It is a hard oval ball spun within a leaf from a single thread hundreds and hundreds of feet long. When finished its walls are stiffened by a liquid which the caterpillar exudes for the purpose. The cocoon may be found on a tree swinging by a short silken ribbon, or on the ground beneath if the attachment has proved insufficient or if the insect has chosen to go to the earth before pupating.

The inmate of the first cocoon of this kind that I ever saw escaped death by the merest good luck, for when I discovered that there was absolutely no opening in the cocoon, I concluded that its builder had blundered, and so cut a door-way. Later I learned that I had not been of the least service to the Poly-phemus, for these moths know exactly how to proceed when

Photograph by Snyder

Polyphemus cocoons, showing the manner in which they are attached to the tree

ready to emerge. Each then secretes an acid solution which softens and separates the stiffened threads near its head and thus enables it to step forth with the greatest of ease. I shall never forget the appearance of the moth as it came from this cut cocoon. It was a queer-looking insect; the brown furry legs, tan-colored body, and head with its two feathery feelers were all there big as life, but the wings! why, they were no longer than those of the little white miller moth that flies about one's lamp in the evening; but Polyphemus wings they were, in color and markings, even if they were small. I started to make a drawing of the insect because its great body appeared so ridiculous with only a kind of shoulder-cape for a covering. Before I had more than an outline, the moth raised and flapped those wings, much as a cock does when it crows, and the wings began to grow larger and larger until they hung way below the body. At first they seemed a bit mussed, but soon the wrinkles disappeared, and there was the Polyphemus in apple-pie order. It had taken just fifteen minutes by the clock to enlarge its mantle. And the "mantle" was of tan lightly dusted with black; bands of black and pink crossed the wings and two great eye-spots peered from the under pair and two smaller ones from those above.

The coloring of the Polyphemus moth, to my mind, is much more exquisite than that of the Cecropia or the Promethea, and, with the exception of the Luna, I consider it the handsomest of our silk-spinners.

Eggs laid by a captured moth on the twenty-ninth of June were as large as those of Cecropia, circular in shape, and, when cleansed of the dark adhesive glue, white with a brown equatorial band.

The larvæ gnawed their way out of the shells on July eighth and ate the greater portion of them before taking other food. They are not at all finical as to their diet and will devour nearly anything offered in the "green-goods" line; possibly the mother moth knows this, for she is more careless in the selection of plants and places on which to deposit her eggs than is the Cecropia.

The young Polyphemii were much like the Lunas in size and shape, with pale-green bodies, yellow tubercles, and dark heads. They are delicate and difficult to rear because they

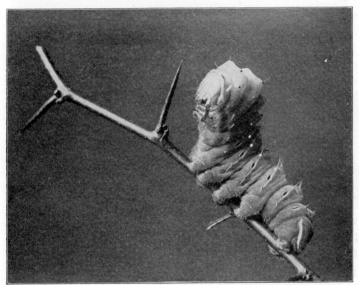

Photograph by Lustig

A partly-grown caterpillar

suffer not only from the attacks of parasites but also from a disease of the tubercles.

When one does secure fully grown larvæ, however, they are found to be exceedingly handsome fellows with blue-green bodies, brown heads, diagonal side-marks of lemon-yellow, orange spiracles, and four rows of metallic tubercles that glint like gold in the sunlight. This gold, however, is nowhere to be seen when the insect comes forth in its tan-colored mantle.

CHAPTER VII

A CATERPILLAR WITH WEAPONS OF DEFENCE

THE Io, *Automeris io*

"I should like just the chance once to show you
How lovely a moth can appear,
Who has slept undisturbed in his casket
His little two-thirds of a year."

IT is useless to deny that certain species of caterpillars defoliate the trees on which they feed, but the larvæ of many varieties live isolated lives, and the green stuff which each consumes is not of sufficient quantity to injure the food plant even in appearance. The popular belief is well fixed in the minds of most of us, however, that all caterpillars are harmful, and not only harmful but poisonous, while the fact is, only a very few of the family are able to inflict a personal injury, and these can be easily recognized after a little study.

One of the group, the Io, is a common larva that should be avoided, for when touched the spines exude an acid and this causes a stinging sensation, the pain of which, however, is never of long duration.

This action of the spines may be performed without volition on the part of the insect, but my experience with one family leads me to believe that the Io can retard or accelerate the flow of this irritating fluid. I found after caring for the caterpillars for two weeks that they no longer stung me when I changed

Photograph by King
A. I discovered two families upon a wild cherry tree B. They travelled single file, close together

their food leaves, and, naturally, I wondered whether or not they connected the daily handling with their supply of fresh food.

My introduction to the insect occurred on the sixteenth of a certain July, when I discovered two families, one possibly a week older than the other, upon a tree of wild cherry. In each colony the caterpillars rested with their heads toward the edge of the leaf, and *en masse* they appeared quite like a woolly rug.

I broke off the twigs holding them and upon reaching the house placed these in a bottle of water; for it

The mature green Io

is essential that caterpillars in confinement be constantly suppled with fresh food leaves.

Upon examination I found that the heads of the larvæ were of a warm brown, the bodies of a yellow-brown with three pale

lines on either side, while on each larva there were clusters of bristles arranged in six lateral rows. All of the insects bore the same markings and colors, but the younger members of the group, measuring one-fourth of an inch in length, were less conspicuous.

I had read that young Io caterpillars frequently travel with military precision, so I was not surprised but only greatly entertained the next day when my captives became restless and later formed in line. Two of the larger and two of the smaller Ios started up the petiole of a leaf; they went up and back several times, always

Opened cocoon, showing moth in act of coming from pupa case

in the same order, then down the main stem a short way, returned to the leaf, described a half-circle on its upper surface, and then disappeared beneath.

It did look to me as if the four were Io generals reconnoitering. The other caterpillars began to move; they travelled single file, close together over the pathway of the leaders, but they journeyed farther down the main stem of the twig before turning. It chanced that the line of march up, in passing about the stem, twice intercepted the army as it came down, but when this occurred there was no confusion among the individuals, no crawling under or over each other, and no leaving of the ranks. The returning caterpillars appeared to have the right of way, for the down-coming line halted in perfect order, a break was made, and through this opening the up-moving body passed to the leaf where their "generals" had described the half-circle. At this point in the journey a seeming mutiny arose. Some of the insects declined to "go below," and at length there was a great upheaval and commotion. The four who had directed the march reappeared and entered into the *mêlée*. I regret that a call prevented me from seeing how the refractory Ios were subdued,

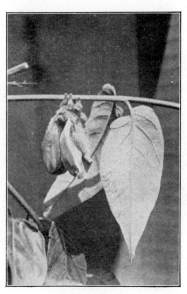

The male just emerged

but an hour later I found the entire number contentedly feeding in their usual mat form on the under side of the very leaf which had been the scene of the "mimic mutiny." These caterpillars, as far as I know, did not again attempt to travel in company; possibly after this march in confinement they realized that they were in quarters too cramped for military manœuvres.

At the end of a month the older Ios were two inches in length and of a beautiful green color; their spines were tipped with black, and on each side of the body there was a conspicuous pink line edged below with white. The caterpillars were not particular as to their food, being quite willing to eat leaves

Photographs by McKay

We turned the camera upon him—   —and continued to photograph him—

of corn, ailantus, dogwood, and poplar, if wild cherry was not within reach, and this made it much easier to care for them.

On August twentieth one Io became restless, grew dull in color and somewhat shrunken in appearance. Soon it began to spin its cocoon, using a leaf for the foundation.

The last of that family went into winter quarters on September nineteenth, and it was the fourteenth of the following June before any of them reappeared. Then I discovered that a male and two females had discarded their silken blankets. The male, a bright canary-yellow in color, had just emerged. By the time he had ascended a twig, and before his wings were entirely "unfurled," we turned the camera upon him and continued to photograph him until he was ready to fly. The females were somewhat larger than the male and entirely different in color, being of a soft reddish-brown;

—until he was ready to fly

they had the big eye-spots on the hind wings, however, the hall-mark of these insects.

One female began to oviposit on the fifteenth, and on the twenty-first her eggs were a deep yellow with a dark spot in each; later, I learned that the black head of the larva is responsible for this spot. The eggs grew dark before hatching, because the yellow-brown bodies of the caterpillars showed through the transparent shells.

The females were larger and entirely different in color

51

They had the big eye-spots on the hind wings

The caterpillars donned pale-green skins

A few hours after the larvæ had emerged and before they had eaten I saw fifteen of them travel along the edge of a leaf to its apex, then down the midvein to the base and up the opposite side of the leaf for half of its distance, where they arranged themselves in the form of a mat.

I gathered Ios, at random, from the vivarium and placed them on this leaf, but apart from the others. They quickly formed in procession and began to journey to and fro until at length they crossed the track of their relatives—probably a microscopic silken pathway—on to this they turned and, moving rapidly, joined the first-mentioned group of tiny caterpillars.

These Ios moulted when they were seven days old, and two weeks later for the second time. Then, with the appearance of the light side lines, their likeness to the first-found larvæ became apparent.

In another week the caterpillars donned pale-green skins which grew more vivid with the fourth and last moult, and by September first all were immured within their cocoons.

CHAPTER VIII

ODD DOINGS UNDERGROUND

THE IMPERIALIS, *Basilona imperialis*

"Yet wert thou once a worm, a thing that crept
On the bare earth, then wrought a tomb and slept."

IT seems strange that certain caterpillars deliberately bury themselves alive, but it is a fact. In the fall, if we keep our eyes open, we may see how several varieties dig, burrow, and disappear into the ground.

Basilona imperialis, one of the largest, lives upon many common trees, but manages to remain an inconspicuous object among its food leaves largely because when its brown or dark-green body is at rest its color, modelling, and position make it seem very like the twigs of the tree on which it feeds.

It was two years before I found the caterpillar and then I saw one eating pine needles. Its resemblance to the stem on which the needles grew was such that I should have overlooked the larva if I had not been searching for the species.

My elation over the find and my anxiety to examine it at once would not admit of my confining the specimen in a collecting box, so I picked the spray on which it fed and in this way carried the imperial crawler home. Apparently, it did not realize that anything unusual had occurred, for it continued to eat pine needles during the entire trip—a performance that was both entertaining and amusing. As soon as it had finished with one needle it would grasp another between its feet and bend this back until the tip touched its mouth, when it would eat the suc-

culent dainty much as a child eats stick-candy, and down to the very last bite.

Three or four days after the capture of the Imperialis it dis-appeared into the piece of sod provid-ed for the purpose. But as I was curious

Photograph by Snyder
The pupa of the Imperialis (a large specimen)

to see the chrysalis of the insect, I dug up the one into which this caterpillar turned and found a brown, shiny pupa not unlike that of the Luna, but of greater length.

It is not wise to disturb such "buried treasures," however, for interference with their normal condition is quite apt to cause the death of the insect, as it did in this case.

The loss of the Imperialis made me doubly anxious to secure other specimens, and knowing that the moth frequents electric lights, I described it to the man who takes care of the lights in our neighborhood and asked him to save any living specimens which he might find, with the result that early in July he brought me several moths, but all were males. I had almost de-spaired of getting a female or her eggs when, on the twelfth of the month, a neighbor, in passing through a vacant lot where a pine tree grew, noticed a robin pecking at a moth which lay on the ground helpless from a broken wing. She rescued the insect and sent it over to the "butterfly lady." It proved to be the much desired female. Like the males, she was of a beautiful canary-yellow with heliotrope markings, but the markings were less pronounced. This moth measured seven inches from tip to tip of her fore wings, but her thin body indi-

Male moths (one-half life size)

cated that she had deposited most of her eggs. She laid forty, however, during the twenty-four hours preceding her death. They were of a honey-yellow color and larger than those of Cecropia. A few days after they were deposited, a red line appeared in each, and all of the eggs turned dark before the little crawlers gnawed their way out, which they did on the morning of the twenty-fourth. The caterpillars at birth were one-fourth of an inch long and of a yellow-brown color. Their tubercles were mere dark specks, but these began at once to grow in a remarkable manner; five minutes after a larva hatched some of the tubercles would be three-sixteenths of an inch in length and much branch- ed. When these tubercles were fully formed a larva would turn and de- vour all or part of its egg shell, quite

One young larva feeding on hemlock

as I had seen the Polyphemus do, and I did not find that a little Imperialis ever made a mistake as to which was its own shell.

I watched the caterpillars through a magnifying glass. They spun a good deal of silk as they moved hither and thither, and as they were restless and quarrelsome the fine threads soon became wrapped about the wee bodies and entangled in the branched spines. It seemed as if the insects were being caught in a web of their own weaving.

For hours they showed no inclination to eat, although I provided elm, pine, maple, sycamore, oak, sassafras, wild cherry, butternut, hickory, and hemlock, all of which are said to be favorite food plants of the larvæ. Finally, two fed on the hemlock and lived, the other thirty-eight died—starved, so to speak, in the midst of plenty.

But in the face of this disaster I still had hopes of securing the life history of the Imperialis, for another piece of good fortune had come to me in a second female moth, found near an electric light, on the night of July twenty-sixth, and by the husband of the woman who had sent me the broken winged specimen. Had it not been for her find, I should have missed the second moth in all probability, but the man had become interested.

The eggs of the second moth were laid in a vivarium on strips of netting, and they began to hatch twelve days later. I had a bottle of fresh maple leaves ready for the crawlers when they emerged, then, without disturbing them, I removed the net covering of the box and replaced it with the glass. This proved a most satisfactory arrangement, for it prevented the escape of the young larvæ while it enabled me to watch their development.

As the caterpillars grew they did not change greatly in appearance, except that their breathing holes during different moults were outlined in light brown, green, and white.

These caterpillars, between three and four hundred in number, retained their brown color from start to finish, although green individuals are sometimes seen. It was no small undertaking to care for this imperial family, still they paid for their keep in the pleasure which I derived from my study of them.

The caterpillars had marked characteristics; for example, before each moult a larva would cling to the under side of a twig with the front portion of its body so lifted and curved that it seemed as if the back of the creature must break. I once found two caterpillars that had assumed this peculiar pose, close together and facing each other, so I photographed them, and discovered later that if the picture was viewed down-side up the insects seemed to be reared as for mortal combat, while in reality both were in a very helpless condition.

Speaking of photographs, one caterpillar proved especially

interesting while it was being caught by the camera. As the shutter clicked this crawler decided to feed, so it moved from the twig where it had been to the petiole of a near-by leaf which, of course, sagged under its weight. This caused the larva to "back step" to the twig, where, clinging by its pro-

Photograph by Lustig

This picture is viewed down-side up, and the insects seem to be reared as for mortal combat

legs, it stretched its body until the edge of the leaf was barely within reach. It nibbled a few bites from this, but the position was too uncomfortable to be retained, so, ceasing to eat, the caterpillar assumed a wise, sphinx-like attitude, in which it remained for several moments; then suddenly it began to bite into the petiole of the leaf, and in such a way that it made a groove around half of its circumference. To my surprise, the larva next caught the leaf in its jaws and pulled upon it until the petiole broke at the weakened place. The leaf did not fall, however, for a sufficient number of fibres had been left in the stem to prevent its doing so; instead, the edge of the leaf came within easy reach of the insect, which began at once to dine.

Was this clever manœuvre of the Imperialis the result of some past experience, and therefore a so-called intelligent act, or

Photograph by Lustig

It stretched its body until the edge of the leaf was barely within reach

only a chain of impulses instinctively performed? In either case, the "worm" responded to the silent command of a controlling Intelligence.

There were, of course, accidents in so large a family of caterpillars, but a goodly number survived and burrowed into the ground, the last disappearing on October twelfth.

When the moths began to emerge the following summer, I found the undertaking was not as difficult as I had imagined it would be, because the caudal and side hooks on the pupa cases push them upward until the portion covering the head of the insect is at the surface where it can be easily lifted by the awakened moth, which then steps forth, seemingly with perfect ease.

Male and female Imperialis moths

CHAPTER IX

THE BIOGRAPHY OF A ROYAL MOTH

THE REGALIS, *Citheronia regalis*

"Earth's crammed with heaven,
  And every common bush afire with God,
  But only he who knows takes off his shoes."

TO the uninitiated, the terms "Royal Walnut" moth and "Hickory Horn-devil" caterpillar naturally suggest two creatures as diverse as possible from each other, but the fact is, the names are descriptive of and applicable to the same insect, *Citheronia regalis*, at different periods of its existence.

I made the acquaintance of the Regalis when some amber-colored eggs came to me through the mail. They were larger than any moth eggs I had previously known, and under the glass their surfaces showed facets.

When the caterpillars hatched on the twenty-seventh of July they bore the characteristic markings which are responsible for the insects' common name of "Hickory Horn-devil." Their skins were black, his Satanic majesty's own color, while there were horns, spined horns, in plenty. There were three pairs on the thorax of each larva, and a single one at the caudal extremity, which elongated and took form before my very eyes. A peculiar feature of the horns was a minute spined ball at the tip of each. These balls disappeared, however, when the first skin was cast.

I noticed that the young crawlers, each a half-inch in length, as they began to promenade over the spray of walnut leaves to

which I introduced them, carried their horns erect, but that
later, when resting, they bent the horns of the thorax forward
until their heads were entirely concealed by them. Then not
content with this manœuver, they doubled on themselves, so

Photograph by King   *By courtesy of " Country Life in America "*
They had a decidedly stilted appearance

to speak, and for the time lost their identity as caterpillars
and became to all intents and purposes dark, oval masses of
rubbish.

After the second moult the "Horn-devils" made no effort to
conceal or disguise themselves, but remained exposed upon the
twigs of their food plant. What they might have done on their
native heath I am unable to say, for I reared this valuable
family by hand in a breeding-cage. The caterpillars did well
in confinement, however, and there was not an accident or a
death among them. From the first they had a decidedly
"stilted" appearance, owing to their extremely long and slen-

der prolegs, which lifted the bodies somewhat above the surface on which the insects crawled or rested.

One naturally would expect that the moulting of the "Hickory Horn-devil," with its spined horns, would be a more difficult undertaking than the moulting of a smooth skinned cat-

Photograph by King

After the third moult

erpillar; but such was not the case, for the horns withdrew readily from the old covering, and in perfect condition.

After a caterpillar was freed from its ruptured skin it would always turn and slowly devour it, leaving only the face mask—usually shed at the beginning of the moult—which, no doubt, was too tough a morsel for the jaws of even this, our largest native caterpillar.

With the third moult the dark skins of the larvæ were replaced by others, in which were tones of orange, salmon, blue, and green, and these colors were retained after the fourth moult, so that a mature caterpillar measuring five and a half inches in length became a conspicuous object.

THE BIOGRAPHY OF A ROYAL MOTH

On the second day of September one of my "Royal" family grew restless, and that evening I found a small pool of liquid in the bottom of the box, which indicated that the creeping days of the larva were numbered. I knew that it needed earth in which to conceal itself, but this I was unable to pro-

Burrowing caterpillars smooth and cement the walls of their cells

vide for another twenty-four hours, and by that time the Regalis had expelled so much fluid that it was quite shrunken, and its prolegs were shrivelled and useless. It could neither crawl nor cling to a support, and made no effort to go into the ground, which it would have done a day earlier.

All the burrowing caterpillars that pass the chrysalis period in subterranean cells smooth and cement the walls of these cells in order to keep the earth from crumbling and suffocating them during their helpless pupa state, and no doubt the liquid discharged by my specimen would have been used for this work. If so, did the "Horn-devil" realize, after the loss, that it would no longer be able to prepare properly its pupa cell? Be this as it may, the larva remained exposed and gave me the opportunity of seeing it discard its "long clothes." This appeared to be a difficult undertaking, which was not

Photograph by King
The wings, antennæ, and legs of the future moth show quite plainly

accomplished until the fifth of the month, when at ten o'clock in the forenoon the skin opened and the chrysalis emerged rapidly. At first, it was soft and of a yellowish-green tone, the

A caterpillar five and one-half inches in length

wings, antennæ, and legs of the future moth showing quite plainly as they lay folded upon the breast; but by evening the surface was hard and of a dark brown color.

Royal moth, the Regalis

I gave the remaining caterpillars earth in which to crawl when they were ready to pupate, and by the end of the month all had disappeared.

During the first week of the following July I saw one of the "Royal" moths make its bow to the world, and I must say I was disappointed in its appearance, for after it had left its chrysalis shell, crawled up a twig, and shaken down its wings it proved to be "royal" in size, but its brown and yellow color seemed very ordinary as compared with the green, blue, salmon, orange, and black of its earlier existence.

CHAPTER X

THE RIDDLE OF THE INSECT PITCHER

THE SEXTA, *Protoparce sexta*

"Above the nicotiana's blooms,
    Narcotic horns, it waves its plumes
    Made drowsy by the drugged perfumes."

A FARMER brought it to me with the information that
he frequently ploughed such things up in the spring,
and that in his neighborhood they called them pitch-
ers, because each had a handle on its side. Could I tell him
what it was? Yes, I could tell him, but to this day I feel
certain that he went away under the impression that I was
jesting or endeavoring to conceal my ignorance about the fine
pupa case of our common Tomato worm, *Protoparce sexta*,
which he had discovered.

This chrysalis is similar to those of the Imperialis and Regalis, save that the long tongue of the enclosed moth is protected by a separate sheath, which in shape and position does
resemble, to some extent, the handle of a pitcher.

One often discovers these hard brown chrysalides while
working in the garden, especially if tobacco, potatoes, or toma-
toes have been grown in the vicinity. And if a specimen is kept
until its inmate emerges, the inmate is found to have very
prominent eyes, stiff, club-shaped antennæ, and a tongue from
three to four inches in length. Along the back of the abdomen
there are conspicuous markings of yellow and black, but in
time the developing wings conceal these vivid colors. The
thorax, wings, and other portions of the moth are clothed with

gray scales of varying shades, and we frequently find the insect at rest upon a tree's gray trunk, where, among the lights and shadows of the bark, it is scarcely noticeable.

The Sexta is a "hawk" or "humming-bird" moth, so called because moths of its kind fly with the swift, strong movements

Photograph by King
The inmate is found to have very prominent eyes and club-shaped antennæ

of the hawk, and they poise above the blossoms as do the humming-birds. Unlike the silk moths, they have well developed mouth-parts, and their tongues probe many a narrow corolla which opens after the butterflies have gone to sleep. Were it not for such moths some of our most cherished blossoms would be obliged to alter their floral arrangements or become extinct, as they depend entirely upon the visits of these night-flying insects for the distribution of their pollen.

While the Sexta moths enjoy the feast which the blossoms offer, they do not neglect the important work of egg laying. In July the farmer is likely to find his tomato vines more or less infested with caterpillars, great green "worms" with a prominent horn at the caudal extremity. The use of this appendage is problematical, for it has no sting and consequently is harmless.

As a rule, the crawlers so resemble their food leaves in color and texture that one is liable to touch them unwittingly while gathering the fruit. A conspicuous black variety is occasionally encountered, but thus far it has escaped my personal notice, possibly because, disliking Tomato worms, I rarely search for them. I realize that they are harmless, perfectly harmless, newspaper stories to the contrary notwithstanding; still I object to having them snap and spit out undigested food at me, as they do when I clean and provision their vivariums.

They are the most pugnacious of all the larvæ which I have studied, and a great contrast in disposition and looks to their gentle mannered and quietly garbed parents.

Were it not for parasitic enemies I fear we should be obliged to wage a deadly war upon these insects, but the little Braconids, tiny

Photograph by King

The gray moth of the "Tomato worm" on the bark of a tree

winged creatures, as a rule, make this unnecessary, for they deposit their eggs under the skin of the caterpillar, and when these hatch the maggots feed upon its body until they no longer require nourishment. When fully grown the parasites come to the surface, and each, standing upon its caudal extremity, begins to weave a fairy structure of pure white silk, the cocoon in which it is to await the development of its small wings.

Photograph by King

They are the most pugnacious of all the larvæ which
I have studied

The rapidity with which these wee creatures emerge and envelop themselves in these cocoons is surprising. I have fed an apparently healthy caterpillar and in two hours found it literally covered with these Braconid cocoons that are erroneously believed to be the eggs of the insect by many who are not familiar with its life history.

About three days are required for the maturing of the adult Braconid; then it cuts a neat little lid at the top of its cocoon, pushes this up, and sallies forth gayly with its brothers and sisters.

But the spent and dying Sexta which has nourished it, still weighted with the swaying empty cradles, will never know the joy and freedom of a winged existence.

Photograph by Bash

CHAPTER XI

A "WORM" OF PROMISE

The Modesta, *Pachysphinx modesta*

"The Sphinx-moth clothed in downy hues,
    In woolly whites and fawns and blues,
    Goes fluttering through the evening dews."

SOME eggs of the Modesta moth, laid on July second, were sent me by mail a few days later, and when received were of a beautiful violet color. This color gradually changed, however, because the green of the caterpillars as they developed showed through the shells, while a bit of red that appeared in each proved later to be the caudal horn of the insect.

The first larva that ate through its shell rested for some moments with only its head exposed. This gave me a fine opportunity to study the mouth parts, especially as they were in constant motion.

A caterpillar has a small upper lip, or labrum, and a narrow under lip, or labium, with a tiny spinneret below; between these lips are the jaws, two pair, and they are attached to the sides of the face so that they work with a lateral instead of a vertical motion. The upper pair, the mandibles, have cutting edges more or less notched into teeth, and these jaws bite portions from the food leaves, while the under jaws, or maxilla, probably assist in the work of preparing the food. The edge of the leaf is held perpendicularly and at right angles to the jaws by the front feet of the larva, which is thus enabled to eat rapidly and in comfort.

There are no fangs or poison glands in the mouth of a caterpillar, and the spread of the jaws is so slight that the mandibles can bite only into thin or loose surfaces.

When these facts are once understood we realize how im-

The granulated skin was a characteristic of the Modesta

possible it is for the insect to inflict a personal injury with its mouth, and in consequence lose to some extent our dread of these crawlers.

The Modestas devoured at least a portion of their egg shells before they commenced to eat regularly, one little crawler nibbling at its late home for twenty minutes before it began upon the fresh poplar leaves which I had placed within its reach.

At birth these caterpillars had rough, green skins, with minute black hairs upon their backs, and each flaunted a red caudal horn. They were truly "cute" when they rested with their last pair of prolegs on a support and their bodies held nearly erect in sphinx-like attitudes. They grew rapidly and were a half-inch long when they cast and ate their first skins. Oblique side-marks of yellow granules ornamented the new skins, and granules were also to be seen on other parts of the bodies. Four days after the first moult the second occurred; then the side lines on the thoraces became much more pronounced and the caudal horns lost their color.

The granulated skin was a characteristic of the Modesta larvæ and even more noticeable after the third moult. With the fourth moult, the granules became white, giving to the caterpillars a frosted appearance. Their faces at this time were of a pinkish purple color, and this color was repeated in their legs and at the tips of their prolegs. It seemed difficult for the caterpillars to cast their face masks when moulting, and thirty-six hours were sometimes needed in which to accomplish the task.

Mature Modesta larva

Although the larvæ, four in number, hatched on July tenth, they did not pupate on the same day. Two disappeared into the ground on August eleventh and a third on August twelfth; all, at this time, were more than three inches in length. The fourth and last crawler showed no desire to burrow into the earth, but remained upon the surface, and seven days later the form of the pupa could be seen through its skin. This skin burst on the twenty-first at seven in the morning. When the pupa—apple-green in color—emerged, its segments were deeply divided, and the wings, head, and antennæ free. The space

Female moth

between the wings was considerable, while the eyes, of a greenish tone, were dotted with red. A green liquid exuded from the insect and immediately spread over its entire body, forming a transparent coating. By eight o'clock the wings lay closely folded at the sides and the abdominal segments had contracted into shape under the varnish-like covering. One antenna remained free for a time, but at one o'clock I found it safely tucked away between the wings. Here also was the tongue, for the Modesta pupa does not have a separate tongue-sheath like that of the Tomato worm.

The chrysalis twisted and turned repeatedly during the day, as if seeking a more comfortable resting-place; but in the morning it was quiet and I spread some loose moss over it and buried the flower pot of earth containing it and the other Modesta pupæ under a breeding cage from which I had taken the bottom boards. The following spring I removed the moss and, to my disgust, I saw that the common black garden ants had been feeding upon the pupæ beneath. A few of the ants were still searching for a last morsel in the empty shells. Further investigation proved that the other pupa cases had also been attacked and their inmates killed.

As I had failed to rear the moths I hoped to secure specimens in June, but only one was taken, a female. She was in very good condition, however, and posed for a photograph.

While the Modesta and the Tomato worm moths are both humming-bird moths and belong to the same family, *Sphingidæ*, they are several degrees removed from first cousins.

The cut of the wings and the shape of the body are quite different, while the length of the tongue is another distinguishing feature, that of the Modesta being too short to sip honey from any but shallow nectaries. This moth wears quiet grays, as does the Tomato worm, but in the gray we find tones of olive, on the hind wings there is a deep, dull pink and a patch of greenish-blue which, together with the sombre hues, make of the whole a beautiful and harmonious color scheme.

CHAPTER XII

THE BIOGRAPHY OF A BUMBLEBEE MOTH

The Diffinis, *Hœmorrhagia diffiinis*

"The velvet nap which on his wings doth lie,
The silken down with which his back is dight,
His broad out-stretched horns, his hairy thighs,
His glistening colors and his glorious eyes."

MANY of us are familiar with that old fashioned shrub which grows in old fashioned gardens, the snowberry bush, *Symphoricarpos racemosus.* When we were children we liked to pick sprays of its fruit for the china vases on grandmother's high parlor mantle, and, best of all, we liked to make necklaces of the white waxen berries.

In those days we never found any black horned green caterpillars upon the bushes, but we saw them later when we began to study insects. I have since wondered what we should have done had we chanced upon a crawler, probably thought it as pretty as the berries and more interesting, for naturally children are unafraid of creeping things.

We made the acquaintance of this larva when it hatched from a blue egg which we discovered on the under side of a snowberry leaf.

At the time we were uncertain as to the egg's identity but thought it would eventually develop into one of the Clearwing Bumblebee Moths.

Strange to say, a few days after we had secured our specimen we received another one, and from the same variety of bush, but the bush grew at Vinton, Iowa, hundreds of miles away.

Both eggs hatched on May twenty-third, that from Vinton opening a few hours before the other.

These little crawlers were also "cute" when they emerged. They were less than one-fourth of an inch in length, of a deep cream color, and so transparent that the black horn of each showed through the flesh where it was inserted. At first the

A black horned green caterpillar

larvæ ate small holes through the leaves instead of nibbling their edges, and the food gave them a greenish hue.

By the twenty-ninth of the month they had doubled in size and were ready for their first moult. As one emerged safely from the old skin we saw it rear the caudal end of its body and stretch its anal claspers as if it enjoyed being free from the tight covering which it had just shed.

Its horn, legs, and prolegs were colorless, but only for a short time. Soon a purplish hue suffused all of the lower portion of the caterpillar, and the horn became black. In a couple of days, however, the larva was quite uniformly blue-green with a yellow "frill" about its neck, the "frill," in reality, being the slightly roughened front edge of the first thoracic segment.

The other larva after its moult came out entirely black and remained dark until it again cast its skin on June fourth. Then it and its companion, also freshly dressed, were identical, both having pale blue-green bodies with green heads, black mouth parts, horns, breathing holes, legs, prolegs, and a black edge on the anal claspers. The under portion of the bodies were dark, and each caterpillar now flaunted a yellow "frill." When not feeding the larvæ rested on the under side of the leaves along the midveins, where frequently they assumed sphinx-like attitudes.

Their appearance was not changed with the third moult on June tenth, but after this the upper portion of the bodies became pale blue, and this color encircled each of the breathing holes.

The Vinton larva seemed now to "stride" ahead of its companion, eating voraciously and consequently increasing rapidly in size. On the evening of June thirteenth we discovered that it was trying to shed its face mask, which had slipped down over the mouth parts. For some reason the mask remained in this position for another twenty-four hours, when it was dropped and the skin discarded.

Our specimen passed its fourth moult on the sixteenth and was then nearly the size of the other. It had caught up, so to speak, during the two days when the "masked" caterpillar had been unable to feed. By the twenty-first both larvæ measured one and one-half inches in length, and we were unable to tell them apart.

They had been good natured, healthy caterpillars from the beginning, and on this day we were confident that we should carry both to the pupa state, and that very soon.

As neither showed any of the discoloration which precedes the pupa state we felt it was still perfectly safe to leave them unconfined, but we were mistaken. In the morning one Clearwing larva was breakfasting upon the snowberry leaves, the other had gone into retirement, and a long search failed to reveal its hiding place.

We took no chances with the remaining specimen, and it was well that we did not, for that evening it began to spin a slight cocoon amid the leaves in its box.

On June twenty-seventh we found it had turned to a darkbrown chrysalis easily discerned through the silken threads that connected the leaves. It measured one and one-fourth inches and was unusually large when compared with the size of the caterpillar. It was a noisy pupa, and the insect would squirm and wiggle as if impatient to be again in the open. But the moth did not appear for fifteen days, then it proved to be a female with a deep yellow body encircled by a wide, dark band, characteristic of *axillaris*, the summer form of a *diffinis*, which is a trimorphic species. A male which developed from a fully grown caterpillar discovered on June thirtieth resembled the female but was more slender, and the yellow scales had an olive tinge.

When I first saw these moths their wings were transparent. In " Caterpillars and Their Moths," written by Ida Mitchell Eliot and Caroline Gray Soule, we are told that these " Clearwings," when first they emerge, have the entire surface of their wings clothed with dark scales, but that the greater number of the scales are shed during the early flights of the insects.

Unfortunately I have never seen the moths leave their cocoons. I should not question a statement made by such careful observers as these women, however, and hope some day to chance upon a black winged Bumblebee Moth.

The insects fly during the day and feast at the flower fountains with the Bumblebees, which they seem to copy in dress and general appearance. They are especially fond of thistle nectar, and late in July specimens can be secured on these blossoms with little effort.

One authority gives the range of the insect "from Canada to Florida and westward to Missouri and Iowa."

It was Mr. Ellison A. Smyth, Jr., of Blacksburgh, Virginia, who found while studying the life history of *Hæmorrhagia diffinis* that the insect has a spring and two summer forms that differ somewhat.

Previous to Mr. Smyth's observations these different forms were considered as separate species. But when he saw the eggs of the spring Diffinis develop into summer forms of the moth and eggs of a summer form into typical spring moths, the question of species was settled beyond a doubt.

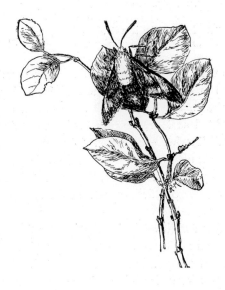

CHAPTER XIII

THE WALNUT SPHINX

THE JUGLANDIS, *Cressonia juglandis*

"And thou, the insect of an hour,
O'er Time to triumph wouldst pretend."

IF fairies used thimbles they would find a beautiful model
for them in the tiny eggs of the Walnut Sphinx, *Cressonia
juglandis*, for these eggs as they rest upon a leaf are, in
shape and pitted surface, very much like the thimbles in my
work-basket. To be sure, each is protected by delicate
hairs, but one must have a good lens in order to see them.

The only eggs, two in number, that I ever found were laid,
not on walnut, but on hickory, and at the extreme tip of the
leaves.

I secured them while searching the tree for three small black
larvæ that I had noticed on one of its upper branches late on
the afternoon of the previous day, and which I hoped would
prove to be "Hickory Horn-devils," although I realized that it
was early in the season for them.

As the caterpillars were hidden among the leaves, I clipped
off small branches from the neighborhood where they had been
with a pair of shears attached to an eight-foot handle. At
length I brought down the crawlers, but to my disgust they
were Cecropias. The experience taught me, however, that
hickory can be added to that insect's long list of food
plants.

Now, while this trip into the country did not yield me the larvæ of the Horn-devils, it was quite worth while, for it gave me the eggs and a few small caterpillars of Juglandis which I might never have found but for the pruning shears, this larva being a species that prefers to live among the high branches of its food tree.

In the book "Caterpillars and Their Moths" the eggs of Juglandis are said to hatch in from seven to eight days. The little crawlers came from those which I had secured on July fifteenth, and before they emerged they could be easily seen through the transparent shells. They had triangular heads sharply pointed at the top; their bodies were a pale yellow and granulated, as were also the caudal horns.

These larvæ grew very restless before they shed their first skins on July nineteenth. After this moult they were intensely green except for faint yellow obliques, pale subdorsal lines, and dark horns. Their anal claspers were long and extended well back—a peculiarity which these larvæ retained to the end of their creeping days.

With the second moult, on July twenty-fifth, a geometrical pattern formed by the side obliques appeared along the back of each caterpillar, the pointed head assumed a brown tip, and the pale granules of the skin were more noticeable. The Juglandis always rested on or near a midvein when it was ready to cast its skin, and held its head so that the apex with its brown point was well in advance of the jaws and in line with the back, a position that slanted the face toward the body. When the mask parted the larva withdrew the upper portion of its head, and then for a time looked most grotesque with the old mask clinging to its jaws.

The caterpillars grew slowly, and after the third moult, on August first, were only one and one-sixteenth inches long.

One caterpillar had great difficulty in shedding its fourth skin and was unable to eat for forty-eight hours. At five P. M. of August seventh it became free. The other had moulted the previous day. Their appearance was now greatly altered, for the heads were less pointed and the bodies somewhat

The Juglandis ready to cast its skin (about two-thirds life size)

elliptical, tapering both ways from the sixth and seventh segments, while the skins were ornamented with dots of yellow ochre arranged in bands, and I found that larger-sized dots were responsible for the obliques.

It was at this period in the Juglandis's history that I heard first the peculiar hissing noise which the caterpillar makes when annoyed or disturbed, and, to say the least, the experience was startling.

As the larvæ matured their skins darkened somewhat, a fact due in part to the brownish circles which appeared around the yellow dots, and with this darkening the insects became quite like the under side of the walnut leaves. Is it protective coloration by means of which the slow-growing larvæ keep in tone with their withering food plants?

The Juglandis is said to eat not only walnut but butternut and hop-hornbeam and, as I discovered, hickory leaves. A day came when none of these were at hand, so I substituted elm, and it was eaten without the slightest hesitancy. Then I noticed that the foliage of the elm, like that of the other food trees, had lost much of its green color.

By August fifteenth the caterpillars were two and one-half inches in length. Then they ceased feeding, grew dull in tone, and two days later crept down into the earth provided for them.

On August nineteenth the caterpillars had not yet turned, and they resented my investigation of their quarters. But on the twenty-second they had disappeared, and in their places were two pupæ, one an inch and a third in

Pupa showing spines on certain segments

length, the other somewhat larger. The surface of these pupæ was rough to the touch owing in part to the stiff spines that edged certain segments, while a feature peculiar to them was the flattening beneath of the anal segments.

Pupa showing the flattening of the anal segments

The pupæ were packed in moss, placed in a cool room, and occasionally sprinkled during the winter. Had I not wished to see and photograph a Juglandis in this period of its life I should have left the earth into which the larvæ burrowed undisturbed. Fortunately, however, the insects lived, and the following June a male and a female moth appeared. In this

Male and female moths

case the male was a light pinkish-brown, banded and marked with deeper shades, and with a square of this color on the inner edge of each fore wing. He measured two and a half inches across when spread, being smaller than the female, which is always the case.

She was clothed with light tan ornamented by brownish-olive and had the merest suggestion of a square on the fore wings.

THE WALNUT SPHINX

These moths, I am told by a friend who has reared several broods of them, vary greatly in shade and intensity of color. And I found this to be the case with the few specimens that developed from the caterpillars which I had secured on that July day when I went hunting for "Horn-devils" with the pruning-shears.

I brought down the crawlers; to my disgust they were Cecropias

CHAPTER XIV

AN UNEXPECTED CHERSIS

The Pen-Marked Sphinx, *Hyloicus chersis*

"Simple and sweet is their food; they eat no flesh of the living."

THE moth eggs labelled "*Ceratomia undulosa*" came from a butterfly enthusiast, who said they were found on an ash tree. They were about the size of Promethea eggs, and while two were pale green, the third was light yellow. This yellow egg hatched on July seventeenth, and the others six days later.

The crawlers at birth were buff with black caudal horns, and as I found it inconvenient to feed them on ash I gave them instead lilac, a food plant reported to be used by this species. It proved acceptable, for the little crawlers soon started to eat holes through the leaves.

Never doubting the identity of the caterpillars, I began to record their doings, and not until I unearthed the first pupa formed did I realize that the insect under observation could not be *C. undulosa*, for according to good authority, *C. undulosa* would have its tongue resting between the wings and protected by the body covering, while the pupa before me had the tongue in a case of its own. What had I been rearing? After searching the works of several writers on the Lepidoptera, I read in "Caterpillars and Their Moths" accounts of *C. undulosa* and also of *Hyloicus chersis*, and found that both insects are much alike during their larval state, but that they can be readily distinguished in the pupa form by the manner in which the tongue is protected, that of *H. chersis* being always in a separate sheath.

Now to go back to the three small larvæ which we will call by their proper name of Chersis; one was drowned when but

Photograph by Bash

It seemed to me that from hour to hour I could notice an increase in the size of this caterpillar (two-thirds life size)

a few days old, the others passed through their different periods safely and became perfect moths.

While young, each little fellow rested on the midvein of a leaf, where its long slender body was quite inconspicuous.

The first moult of the older caterpillar occurred in six days, the second in five, the third in three, and the fourth in six days. Then the larva fed for five days more before it went into the ground, and how it did grow during that time!

With the first moult its body appeared sprinkled with tiny white dots that were not raised, however; with the second moult these dots became granules, and at this time two faint subdorsal lines could be seen extending from head to horn.

When the third skin was discarded the caterpillar had a clear grass-green color, which was somewhat darker along the back. The granules were still present as well as seven pairs of yellow obliques, the horn was spined and tipped with black, while the green head, a bit narrower at the apex, showed faint facial lines. Gradually, blue markings appeared above the yellow obliques, each separated from the yellow by a thread of white, and from this time on the Chersis was very sphinx-like in its bearing toward things in general and toward myself in particular, rearing its body haughtily whenever it deemed my investigations of its daily life too personal.

Photograph by Bash
The pupa with its distinguishing tongue-case

For long periods it would cling to a support by its anal claspers peppered with black, and by its second, third, and fourth pairs of prolegs; the first pair extending forward while the thorax of the insect bent down in a very graceful curve.

With the final moult the face lines and blue side-markings changed to black, the horn took on a bluish cast, and the breathing-holes showed orange-red, but somehow they were not conspicuous. It seemed to me that from hour to hour I could notice an increase in the size of this caterpillar, which became nearly four inches long before it ceased feeding on August tenth. It did not change color greatly, and at the end of twenty hours it went into the earth, where four days later I found the freshly formed pupa with its distinguishing tongue-case.

Dr. Holland and Mr. Beutenmüller report this species as

Photograph by King

A tailor-dressed moth

being double-brooded, the former stating that the moths are on the wing in May and again in August, but if this is the case, the two broods must overlap, else how could one find young caterpillars in July?

The Chersis pupæ during the following June yielded the moths, elegant creatures, tailor dressed, and measuring when spread nearly five inches across. Their bodies were black and white with a gray dorsal stripe, and their wings were also gray but of many shades, while on the fore wings were to be seen the black lines which give to the insect its common name of "Pen-marked Sphinx."

Pen-marked sphinx moth at rest

CHAPTER XV

A MINT FEEDER

THE EREMITUS, OR HERMIT, *Hyloicus eremitus*

"Where the bee sips honeyed clover,
And the worm takes toll of mint leaves."

THE word "mint" always brings to my mind's eye the picture of a well known brook that goes babbling gayly through meadows and woods, even in the hot, dry summer time. In a certain pasture the edges of this brook are bordered by the fragrant spearmint and peppermint, green and luxuriant.

When I learned that a sphinx moth, commonly known as the Hermit, and to the entomologist as *Hyloicus eremitus*, oviposits upon these plants, I visited that part of the brook where the mints grow, hoping to find caterpillars, but none were feeding upon the juicy leaves, whose ragged appearance in many places, however, proved that crawlers had been there.

A week later, just at dusk, I took a short cut through this pasture, and as I reached the spearmint I could not resist the temptation to stop and again search for the larvæ. It was well that I did so, for there they were in plain view taking their

95

supper. Accidentally, I had discovered that Eremitus caterpillars have nocturnal habits.

The next morning, before the grass had dried, I revisited the mint bordered brook and systematically began a search for eggs, which I was certain that I should find, for the caterpillars of the previous night were young.

Only those who have laboriously hunted for such small treasures can appreciate this undertaking and my delight when at noon I counted ten small eggs like iridescent pearls in my collecting box. These eggs grew dark, however, before the inmates emerged, which occurred on July thirtieth, thirty-first, and on the second and fifth of August. From the first, the tiny creatures assumed that sphinx-like position which is so suggestive of dignity, reserve, and caterpillar haughtiness.

At birth the larvæ were pale cream color, one-third of an inch long, and each had on its second segment a short pointed horn, and at its caudal end another horn that was two-thirds the length of the body. Soon both of these appendages became black, and after this the outline of the body was somewhat lost.

The young crawlers began life by eating holes in the leaves, and it was several days before they ate their food in the regular way.

As is usual with larvæ, the individual moulting periods of the Eremiti varied somewhat, but all cast their first skins in six days, shed them a second time in from three to eight days, and repeated the performance seven to nine days later. Then, after feeding for three or four days, they underwent their fourth and last moult.

The Eremiti are afforded protective coloration to an unusual degree, for, as the caterpillars develop, designs in shades of brown and rich madder appear upon their green skins, and these designs tend to blur the body form of an insect until it becomes practically invisible among the mint leaves, for these leaves are more or less marred by dry and withered portions which have also the brown and madder tones.

I was especially interested in the thoracic and caudal patterns that appeared upon the larvæ after the third moult, for,

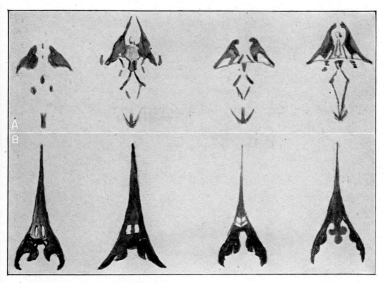

A Thoracic and *B* caudal patterns on partly grown larvæ (three times life size)

while each caterpillar wore practically the same designs upon its back, no two of them had patterns that were identical. In order to show the variations I made drawings from four specimens and found that a pair of birds facing each other, or a bird with lifted and out-spread wings, suggested the motif for the thoracic pattern. In addition to this and the caudal markings, a larva had a dark spot above each proleg, and dark feet, while its sides were crossed by seven light obliques. Truly it was a well disguised caterpillar.

I found one Eremitus had moulted for the fourth time on August eighteenth, and, to my surprise, its appearance was changed entirely, the skin being no longer green with brown markings, but instead, of a dull gray overshot with old rose and olive, which colors formed the woof and warp of an open mesh design traced upon the under "lining." Toward the head this mesh disappeared, and the thorax showed a dull green flushed with rose. Here a triangular black velvet spot edged with light salmon covered the top of segments one, two, and three, and as the horn of the caterpillar was greatly flattened, this spot suggested a pointed cap pulled well over the face. Although the change in color had been so remarkable, there was no mistaking the larvæ.

A still greater surprise was in store for me when, a couple of days later, I saw one of the crawlers undergo its fourth moult. Instead of coming out in the dark skin as I had expected, it appeared in one of apple-green marked with delicate heliotrope, and after assuming its characteristic attitude it remained very still while the vent and anal claspers deepened in color, and the thoracic patch darkened and took form within the heliotrope border. From almost the first a delicate woof and warp pattern in greens could be seen on the abdominal portion of the insect, but gradually this assumed the old rose and olive of the other caterpillar; then the body of the larva seemed to fill with a dark fluid, which obliterated this beautiful design, and twenty-four hours later the crawler had become a mud-brown "worm" with only the black "cap" remaining as proof that it was an aristocratic Eremitus.

Some of this family moulted with heads down, others with heads up, and if I reversed a twig to which a member clung it appeared unconscious of the change.

These captive caterpillars disliked sunlight and were as

secretive as conditions would allow, frequently hiding among the stems of the food plant where it was difficult to locate them. I found that these Eremiti would eat wild bergamot, and apparently with such enjoyment that occasionally I gave them

Photograph by Bash

The mud-brown "worm" with black "cap"

this food in place of the spearmint. I could not induce the larvæ to even sample peppermint, although it is reported to be a plant on which the caterpillars live.

By August twenty-fifth, two larvæ were four inches in length and very dumpish, so I placed them and the sprig of mint in a flower-pot partly filled with damp sand and covered this with

Pupa (slightly enlarged)

a small plate. On the morning of the twenty-seventh no caterpillars were in sight. I did not believe, however, that they burrowed into the earth, but in order to be certain, I emptied the pot. The crawlers were gone. I searched the room until I found one crushed under a rocker and the other yards away, alive but injured. Foolish Eremiti to go journeying into unknown regions.

This experience taught me, however, that these caterpillars have unusual strength, for singly or together the specimens had lifted the plate sufficiently to pass out between its edge and the side of the crock. I am certain of this, for I know that the crock remained untouched from the time I covered it until I examined it two days later.

A third larva went into the ground on August thirtieth and another on the thirty-first, although neither had reached the size of those that were killed.

A pair of moths

100

In a week I sifted the earth and found two fine pupæ, each one and one-half inches long with short tongue-sheaths. On the sides of the abdomen, just above the spiracles, were three smooth oval disks which were so placed that the segments of the body worked upon them and this enabled the insect to bend easily. The rough anal edges of these disks, together with a sharp caudal spine, help, no doubt, to hold the pupa-case in the ground when the moth is ready to pass into the outer world.

These moths are not large, measuring, with wings spread, from two and one-half to three inches. The male and female are alike in color and markings, the body and wings being in shades of smoky-brown, the under wings are very light edged and crossed by wide dark bands. A characteristic of the insect is a light dot always found near the centre of each fore wing.

Had an Eremitus yellow blotches on its abdomen, it seems to me it might, at first glance, pass for a diminutive Tomato worm moth, so much alike are they in color and form.

The caterpillars that I reared are at this writing still asleep in their earthen tombs, and as the final chapter in their life history cannot be written for another year, I have photographed and described a pair of moths captured at Vinton, Iowa, early in the past June.

CHAPTER XVI

THE UNMASKING OF TWO FRAUDS

THE PANDORUS AND ACHEMON, *Pholus pandorus, Pholus achemon*

"Oh! look thou largely with lenient eyes
   On whatso beside thee creeps and clings
For the possible glory that underlies
   The passing phase of the meanest things."

DURING the summer and fall one sees a great variety of caterpillars. The grape and woodbine are favorite feeding grounds for several species, two of which are especially dreaded by people unfamiliar with the insects. This feeling of repulsion, no doubt, is due in part to the fact that each larva as it reaches maturity shows a great black "eye" at the caudal end of its body, and this end of the body is thought by many to be the creature's head. I have been told more than once that this "eye" rolls wickedly from side to side when a caterpillar is angered, and that the caterpillar hisses and spits out poison if disturbed.

It is all very funny when you know the real facts in the case, and these can be so easily gained through personal observation if there is a grape or woodbine growing in your neighborhood.

If the near-by vine is not infested with the "one-eyed" larvæ, go farther afield for your specimens. Somewhere you will

THE UNMASKING OF TWO FRAUDS

Five pairs of oblique patches upon Pandorus and six pairs upon Achemon

discover them, and when you have done so carry them home and feed them with leaves from the neighborhood vine.

Your find may prove to be Pandorus or Achemon larvæ, insects very closely connected and identical in appearance until after their second moult, when they can be distinguished by the oblique oval patches upon their sides—five pairs upon Pandorus and six pairs upon Achemon.

With this third skin the little caudal horns of these caterpillars also differ slightly, for that of Pandorus curls forward, while that of Achemon stands erect or bends backward.

When the crawlers are about ten days old their third

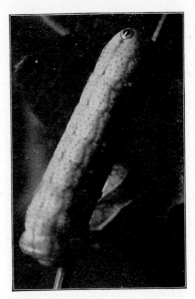

The eye-like tubercle on the caudal end of the larva

103

moult occurs, and with it the "eye-spot" of each becomes apparent, located at the base of the horn. With the fourth moult the horn disappears entirely, and then the "eye" grows and glares in a truly realistic manner; but before this occurs knowledge has robbed the caterpillar of its most effective weapon. We are no longer afraid of this painted sham.

The Pandorus and Achemon, like the Tomato worm and the Modesta, are of the family *Sphingidæ*, but they are in a

Photograph by King

Pandorus

sub-group commonly called "hog" caterpillars, because of a fancied resemblance which the larvæ bear to swine.

Such caterpillars have the third thoracic segment so swollen that it becomes a kind of hood into which the first and second segments are frequently withdrawn. This gives to the insects a cut off appearance and makes the caudal ends of the bodies of Pandorus and Achemon, with their prominent eye-like tubercles, the more noticeable.

These caterpillars belong to the group *Philampelus*, a name meaning "vine lover," and it is most applicable in this case.

If a considerable number of them are domiciled upon a vine, the vine is certain to show the effect of their presence.

Frequently the larvæ grow to be over four inches in length; they vary as to color, some having green and others brown skins, but the oval side-patches are the characteristic feature of the insect.

Some of my specimens burrowed into the ground as early as August twenty-seventh, and others from that date on into October, but no winged adults emerged until the following summer.

Photograph by King

Achemon

These moths, like the Modesta, are quietly garbed in soft, harmonious shades. Pandorus wears velvety olive-greens with a suggestion of pink for contrast, while Achemon dresses in ashes of roses with brown and pink trimmings. They are the moths so frequently seen in the evening poised above the nasturtiums sipping the nectar. Incidentally, they become dusted with pollen grains which they carry from one blossom to another. This service insures cross-fertilization, which is vital to the perpetuation of many plants.

CHAPTER XVII

A GRAPE–VINE FEEDER

THE MYRON, *Darapsa myron*

"Man for thee does sow and plough,
Farmer he, and landlord thou."

THE mother of the first Myron caterpillars which I studied came to me in a glass finger-bowl resting upon a beautiful pink rose. The moth had not been taken upon the rose but had been placed there by an æsthetic friend when she captured it in her garden.

As Madam Myron had already laid a few green eggs, I did not disturb her until she had finished ovipositing.

In six days her little crawlers began to hatch; they were like most young sphinx larvæ, having pale-yellow bodies and long, thin caudal horns. They ate woodbine and grape with equal relish, and moulted first when they were four days old.

Their second moult began on July eleventh, four days later, and they showed no marked peculiarities, excepting granulated skins and face grooves, until after the third moult which occurred on the seventeenth, and then the third and fourth segments assumed a swollen appearance which indicated that the insects belonged with the so called "hog caterpillars."

There was now on each larva two sub-dorsal yellow lines extending from the jaws to the base of the caudal horn. The horn was green-brown and curved backward, the vent showed a yellow outline, and the granules on the body together with the oblique side lines were also of this color. The tips of the feet and the breathing holes were red, while a dark dot had appeared on each proleg.

The larvæ showed no indication of sickness, and as they were confined in glass jars they were not subject to the attacks of ichneumon flies, which is the case with so many Myrons in the open.

Photograph by Bash
Empty pupa case

With the fourth moult there came a very marked difference in color, pattern, and form.

On the twenty-fourth I found one of the family arrayed in its last skin, which was so harmonious in its color combination that I carried it to a fashionable dressmaker in the neighborhood in order that she might see and possibly appreciate the artistic handiwork done by Mother Nature. The lower part of the caterpillar's body and the prolegs were a most exquisite shade of blue-green. The oblique side lines were still present, the last pair extending up on to the horn. These obliques terminated where a pale-blue line edged the wide pea-green dorsal section. The blue flowed down between the obliques and formed a triangle on each segment. The colors were wonderfully soft, and while the markings were distinct they were in no sense crude.

This larva was two inches in length from the jaws to the **tip** of the caudal horn; its swollen segments were very much dilated, and, when discovered, the caterpillar was clinging to the under side of a twig by its second, third, fourth, and anal prolegs, while the remainder of its body was bent backward so that the head nearly touched the tip of the caudal horn.

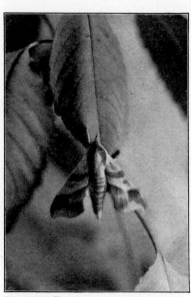

Why these crawlers should prefer what seemingly is so uncomfortable a position is a mystery. Possibly they practice a form of gymnastics which is beneficial to their development, or they may realize that such distorted and strikingly marked bodies serve as a protection to them, for it is unlikely that many bird or beast enemies have sufficient courage to attack a full grown Myron

Photograph by King

During the day the moths remain on some plant, where they seem to sleep

caterpillar, although Miss Eliot and Mrs. Soule report having seen orioles search their vines for the larvæ and eat them in large numbers.

As this brood of crawlers matured, they were as like each other as peas in a pod, and all of the green variety. But others which I have found or reared have sometimes shown decided tendencies toward brown and pink colorings.

On July twenty-ninth some of the larvæ became a dirty

yellow-brown along their backs and dull pink on the sides; they remained quiet on the bottom of the jar for several hours before they began to spin their cocoons of leaves held together with fine silken threads.

One exception I found ten feet away in a corner of the room where the base-boards join. I wondered later if this crawler would have had a sufficient amount of silk in its body to make a cocoon with no leaves for a foundation.

After the caterpillar skins had been discarded, I examined a number of the pupæ. These averaged one and three-eighths inches in length. They were a pale tan-brown with a dark band between the segments below the wing covers. These covers were marked with rows of dark dots as were the eleventh and twelfth segments, while the spiracles were nearly black.

Moths from these chrysalides did not emerge until the following May, but in "Caterpillars and Their Moths" we are told that the authors had one brood of Myrons that pupated in August and appeared as winged adults during the following month.

The moths are about two and one-half inches across the tips of the fore wings; they have a gray-green color marked with olive-green. During the day they remain on some plant where they seem to sleep, but at dusk they visit the flowers and with their long tongues probe the blossoms for hidden sweets.

CHAPTER XVIII

SLY AND SECRETIVE UNDERWINGS

The Catocalas, *Catocalæ*

> "Hurt no living thing:
>   Ladybird, nor butterfly,
> Nor moth with dusty wing,
>   Nor cricket chirping cheerily,
> Nor grasshopper, so light of leap,
> Nor dancing gnat, nor beetle fat,
> Nor harmless worms that creep."

WE all know those loopers, both green and brown, that go measuring half-inches and inches, yards and more yards, as they journey from place to place.

When a very little girl, I remember that one day I nearly went into spasms because a green specimen chanced to promenade over my hand. I also remember that this foolish fear was caused by an old colored mammy's stories of poison worms "that sure will bite and sting de chile."

Now, these looping larvæ travel as they do from necessity, for each has three pairs of its prolegs so aborted that they no longer support the middle portion of the body.

Larvæ of *Catocala*, when young, also walk in this unusual manner, and for the same reason, as some of their prolegs at birth are but partially developed. Later, the mature caterpillars retain to a degree this habit, probably because the props never become sufficiently strong to support the weight imposed upon them.

Catocalæ, like the loopers or *Geometridæ*, simulate, both in markings and colors, the twigs and barks of their food plants,

110

therefore they are rarely found until one has learned when and where to look for them.

A certain variety hides under the shaggy bark of the hickory, another between the grooves on the oak's trunk, while a third, an aspen feeder, is cleverly concealed by the gray-green color of its skin.

The moths of this genus are also protected through coloration, for the gray or brown upper surface of their fore wings usually blends so perfectly with the bark of the trees on which they rest as to make them quite inconspicuous. But wait till a moth flies, then you will probably see bands of yellow, orange, red, rose, or white on its black under wings; it is these markings which give to the Catocalas their common name.

I had never seen Catocala eggs until two varieties, one that of *C. relicta* and the other of *C. amatrix*, were received from Miss Lulu Berry, of Vinton, Iowa.

These eggs, small and somewhat flattened, had meridian lines extending from pole to pole that were intersected by other lines delicate as the threads of a spider web. The eggs of *C. relicta* were the larger, with the gray-green color of the aspen bark on which they had been found. They began hatching on the fourteenth of May. On the following day the first *C. amatrix* appeared. I put a bit of tender aspen leaf into the bottle with *C. relicta*, and gave *C. amatrix* a young leaf of willow. The former at once began to eat the parenchyma from the leaf.

These Catocalas were very active larvæ, and I had been warned that they would escape through exceedingly small apertures, hence I had placed the eggs of each species in a closed bottle. Every day I removed the emerging caterpillars. I must own, however, that the death rate of the insects equalled so nearly the birth rate that by June fourth only one larva, *C. relicta*, remained.

In despair, I wrote to Miss Berry, who replied that her experience with Catocalas had been that the young crawlers need a cool, shady place, and that they will eat only tender terminal leaflets. As the season was unusually warm, and as

Mature larva of *C. relicta* (three-fourths life size)

I had not been sufficiently careful in the selection of "greens," I conclude that it was heat and hunger that killed the caterpillars. Even the one survivor gave up the struggle on June twenty-sixth.

In July, however, I found three fully grown larvæ of *C. relicta* which were unlike any caterpillars that I had previously seen. Each measured three inches in length, was of a light gray suffused with greenish-yellow—a color that seems to protect *C. relicta* through the different periods of its life. The larva had a fringe of hairs below its dark spiracles, a conspicuous mark between the eighth and ninth segments, another on the eleventh segment, and on its head two yellow spots, which showed through a net-work pattern of black. These larvæ became slender, dark-brown pupæ with prominent eye-coverings four days after they had spun. I took two of them to a pho-

The slender, dark-brown pupæ of *C. relicta*
(three-fourths life size)

tographer to be photographed; before I could interfere he had pierced each with the point of a pin in order, he explained, to keep the insects in position.

The moths of *C. relicta* are very light, and, as shown in the illustration, have black and white under wings.

These moths emerge during the summer. I am told that their eggs are laid upon poplar as well as aspen bark, where they remain exposed during the winter.

On July fifteenth I secured a fully grown larva of *C. amatrix*. It had a dark-olive band on either side of the dorsal portion, and this extended from the jaws to the vent. On each segment in this band there was a yellow-brown tubercle. A hump on the eighth segment and a lesser elevation on the eleventh were marked characteristics of the caterpillar. As the specimen escaped after having its picture taken, I lost the moth, but in September I saw several of the pretty creatures upon the bark of willows. Their exquisite rose-barred under wings were concealed, however, by their brown fore wings.

From a captured specimen I secured eggs, which the following year enabled me to carry larvæ of *C. amatrix* into their final moulting period. Then all died, due possibly to the disturbance incident to the cleaning of their cage, for the slightest jar at this time in the lives of larvæ often proves fatal.

Another member of the group, *C. parta*, is frequently seen

Photograph by King

Male and female moths of *C. relicta*

about willows. I shall always have a warm spot in my heart for this species, because it gave me my first life history of the genus. Eggs of this moth were found under the bark of a weeping-willow, and they began to hatch on April twentieth. These Catocalas were less beautiful than some varieties. They behaved well and on June twenty-fifth yielded the first moths. These moths showed "petticoats" of salmon and black, while on each gray thorax there was a very good delineation of a hound's head, with small eyes and long, drooping ears.

Catocala amatrix larva partly grown (slightly enlarged)

Mature *Catocala amatrix* larva (slightly enlarged)

A brown species of *Catocalæ*, with orange and black wings, is *C. neogama;* the caterpillars feed upon the walnut. Miss Berry sent me a few of the larvæ to be photographed; as they posed well I was certain that I should have good pictures of both the mature and the partly grown crawlers. Another dis-

Photograph by King

Upper—*C. cara* moth   Lower—*C. amatrix* moth

appointment was in store for me. That day the heat was so intense that it melted the gelatine of the negatives. Before the condition of the plates was discovered the caudal portion of each caterpillar had become somewhat blurred. Still, I am certain that *C. neogama* could be recognized by these pictures.

Miss Berry had so laughable an experience with a caterpillar of this species that I feel it is worth repeating in her own words: "Finding a big Neogama about nine feet up on a walnut tree, I

Photograph by Bash

Catocala neogama larva partly grown

climbed for him; but at the first touch he sprang off into the air, describing sundry half-circles and acrobatic feats, then landed on my face. While I was glad he landed safely on a soft surface, it took steady nerves not to shake him off as I climbed down the tree." She adds that larvæ of *C. neogama*, when ready to pupate, travel some distance from their food trees before spinning their slight cocoons between leaves.

Caterpillars of two other varieties of *Catocalæ* that feed upon the walnut are *C. piatrix* and *C. palæogama*. The moths of both have orange and black under wings.

Two hickory feeders which I have reared from the eggs are. *C. vidua* and *C. retecta*. They are similar, being dark larvæ, and very like the twigs on which they rest. The black "petticoats" of their moths lack the colored bands characteristic of many of the group.

Photograph by Bash

Catocala neogama larva fully grown

It is said that we have a hundred varieties of *Catocalæ* in the United States. A number of persons are at work upon the genus, among them Miss Berry. She has kindly sent me a list of the species which she has found or reared, together with their food plants. From this list I learn that in addition to the trees already cited we may secure Catocalas from linden, bur-oak, honey locust, and plum, and that the plum feeder, *C. ultronia*, is "just an animated plum sprout, bearing a leaf-bud upon its back."

CHAPTER XIX

ODD INSECT HOMES AND THEIR INMATES

The Bag-Worms, *Thyridopteryx ephemeræformis*

"Every traveller is a self-taught entomologist."

ON the twenty-ninth of April I found the Bag-worm houses, hundreds of them, attached to the twigs of smoke-blackened locust trees, a number of which were already dead, partly because of these Bag-worm visitors, and partly because the lungs of the trees had become choked by soot from the great furnaces in the neighborhood. The smoke from these furnace chimneys had darkened the entire face of nature, while the shacks and small, ugly homes of workmen seemed only to accentuate the desolateness of the scene.

For a brief moment I wondered why one of God's creatures not bound to the location by the necessity of toil, but free to choose the fairest of earth's places for its home, should select this spot. Then I understood. Probably years ago, before the furnaces came, a mother Bag-worm while she was still a caterpillar chanced to hang her queer little dwelling upon one of these locust trees, and later completed her strange metamorphosis within its silken walls. Here, too, her winged mate came courting, and here she laid her eggs, and then, her work finished, the bag that had sheltered her became her burial place, for you must know that the female Bag-worm moth is wingless and never leaves the home which she begins to build in the hour of her birth.

Bag-worm houses

On some fair morning of the next year's June a lot of little crawlers emerged from the tomb of their mother and were soon distributed over the twigs of the locust, and so the colony started.

Year by year it throve and grew in numbers, for the leaves of the trees were never sprayed with poisonous solutions, and the smoke-begrimed bag-shelters kept their inmates immune from the birds; after all, was it not a Bag-worm paradise until the food supply began to fail?

Apparently a few of the caterpillars had realized that they must seek pastures new in order that the generations which were to follow them might have green food stuff, for I found a numer of Bag-worm houses upon a lilac bush some distance from the doomed locust trees.

It must have been a tedious journey for each little emigrant toiling along beneath the weight of its unwieldy domicile. No doubt, weariness, hunger, and thirst were endured, and probably many a "wee one" succumbed to hardships such as have been the lot of all pioneer peoples.

I collected so many of the Bag-worm houses that I found it wise to apportion them among a number of glass jars; I also tied a few in our lilac bush (an unwise action, as I learned later). One jar I kept in a warm room, and its inmates appeared on the afternoon of May twenty-ninth.

They were the merest bits of caterpillars not a sixteenth of an inch in length, very active, and they spun a great deal of silk as they travelled. I found that I could frequently lift a larva by its silken thread, and one individual hung for a second at the end of a piece ten inches long.

The head and thoracic segments of these Bag-worms were dark and shiny, as was the caudal section; the remaining portions were of a brownish tone. The props or prolegs, which usually help to support the abdominal part of a caterpillar, were lacking, and the little crawlers were forced to walk on their six true feet, and as they did so each turned the end of its body toward the head and in this tipped-up position managed to move so rapidly from one part to another of the large paper on which I was examining them that I soon found I must reconfine a portion of the family or lose them all. I noticed that the Bag-worms appeared to go in the direction of the light, so in order to verify this I repeatedly turned the paper, and each time after doing this the wee individuals would also turn so as to again travel toward the window.

When discovered one little crawler had already made its tiny basket for the purpose of protecting the reared portion of its body. This was green and probably was made from bits of dried leaves found in the jar.

While I still watched the manœuvres of the family through a magnifying-glass, I saw a number of the caterpillars begin the weaving of their covers with bits of blue, white, and yellow blotting-paper given them for the purpose. As a rule, a larva chose but one color for its basket; a few, however, used them all, and thus had a parti-colored appearance.

Judging from what I could see, a caterpillar snipped a little pile of fuzz from the paper and felted this with its silk into a small blanket. It then turned a tail-end somersault and caught the blanket on its back and so held it until it had fastened the edges together with silk. At first there was only a narrow strip of covering, but the larva kept adding to this (and always at the front) until the basket was of a depth sufficient to conceal its entire person when desired; usually, however, the Bag-worm walked about with its thorax exposed and with its queer, irregular domicile swaying on its elevated portion behind.

I can think of nothing in the animal world quite so ludicrous as these wee basket-carrying caterpillars tiptoeing over my table.

I found that those members of the family left in the glass jar built their houses with bits taken from the tender bark of the lilac twigs which I had given them for food, and that when not working or walking each little fellow attached itself to a stem or leaf.

I also learned during the first ten minutes of my acquaintance with the Bag-worms that they had a natural inclination toward quarrelling and stealing. For some time I watched a larva not more than two hours old as it pursued, harassed, and bullied one of its family for the possession of the basket it had already made. The undressed individual snapped viciously at the other, tried to entangle it in silk spun, I am sure, for the purpose, and clung to the small basket tenaciously, thus forcing its rightful owner to drag about additional weight. In vain the besieged endeavored to protect its home. It was obliged to surrender to the enemy, and went away doubtless discouraged. I captured and imprisoned it in a small vial with food leaves and a piece of yellow blotting-paper, for I wished to learn if so young a caterpillar had enough silk stored in its body to build at once another shelter. The next morning there was my wee specimen promenading under the new yellow cone of a basket.

But to return to the victorious caterpillar. It tried to take possession of the abandoned domicile, but must have found the task difficult. It could not raise the basket over its head, neither could it back into it, so at length it crawled in head first, expecting, no doubt, to travel right through and thus gain a shelter without further effort, but for some reason the enterprise failed, and the young marauder reappeared and at once departed, leaving another dwelling to be added to the long list of deserted homes. True, this was a very small one, but what do we know of the hopes and fears which the insect had built into its walls?

At the end of the first twenty-four hours I could not find that any of the caterpillars had eaten, unless possibly some had taken their nourishment from the twigs as they masticated the bark to be used in their basket-shelters. However, all were lively and in good condition, judging from the frequent hostilities which I witnessed through my reading-glass.

As I wished to rid the jars of unnecessary material, I took out the bag-houses and examined them to ascertain if any still contained eggs. To my surprise I saw that in quite a number of them there was a brown shell-like chrysalis carefully wrapped in a cobweb blanket of white silk. I concluded that these specimens had died during their pupa period and that there would be no eggs, and was about to dispose of the lot when I noticed a wee crawler issue from the head end of the pupa-case. It made its way through the intricate meshes of the enveloping

silk and was soon followed by another small caterpillar. What did it mean? Were the larvæ the children of some ichneumon fly? No, for they travelled in the same ridiculous tipped-up position as had those which I had found in the jar the day before. I looked carefully at the chrysalis. It showed plainly reddish thoracic segments and dark abdominal ones. Truly, it must be the pupa-case of the Bag-worm, but if so, where was the moth?

They travelled on the under side of a leaf or twig

I was more than glad that I had so large a collection of Bag-worm homes. I could afford to risk spoiling some in order that I might learn this mystery of the insect's life.

My good friend Louise, who is always interested in my investigations, joined me, and together we cut open specimen after specimen. Finally, at the lower end of one bag we found the key to the riddle. It was a head and shrivelled skin, but not of a caterpillar; in fact, the caterpillar skin was still attached to the caudal end of the chrysalis. We had found all that was left of the mother moth. In other bag-houses we discovered similar remains, though, as a rule, they had entirely disappeared.

It seemed that the moths had used their discarded chrysalides as receptacles for their honey-yellow eggs, which we found arranged with great regularity in a mass of fuzzy silk. They were about the size and somewhat resembled those of certain large spiders. When a moth had finished ovipositing there was apparently very little of herself left, and, no doubt, this little frequently disintegrated or dropped to the ground.

As the Bag-worm caterpillars grew, they no longer walked about under their baskets. Instead, they travelled on the under side of a twig or leaf, so that their queer little domiciles swung inverted. These were enlarged from time to time, and the additions were always made at what had become the upper end of the structure. If bits of leaves were used for the purpose there would be seen for a day or so after the enlargement a frill of green about the opening, but many of the larvæ decorated or concealed their silken bags with small pieces so arranged as to give them a thatched appearance.

Photograph by Snyder

In September the Bag-worm houses became stationary

It is a strange protective instinct which causes the insect to disguise with bits of rubbish what might otherwise be a rather conspicuous home. As it is, the Bag-worm houses have more or less the appearance of a spider's nest, but when in the open a bird attempts to destroy one it finds the task difficult because of the tough silken walls behind which, as a rule, the larva is quite safe.

With the coming of September I noticed that one after another of my bag-houses became stationary and that the inmates remained in seclusion. Of course, in a way, I understood what was taking place, namely, that the caterpillars were turning to chrysalides and the chrysalides to moths, and that the wonderful metamorphosis of the insect was being completed behind closed doors.

Later in the month some of the pupæ began to work their way from the lower ends of their bags, and I found that the moths that emerged from these were in all cases males. Unlike their mates, they had wings, delicate gauzy ones, but of sufficient strength to bear each gallant to his lady-love who waited his coming in the seclusion of her darkened home.

CHAPTER XX

A WATER–LOVING CATERPILLAR

The Nymphula, *Nymphula icciusalis*

THERE are some dainty little moths which love the water-ways; so they deposit their eggs upon aquatic plants, and here later their caterpillars feed, entirely or partly submerged.

Personally I had known nothing of the larvæ until I found a species, *Nymphula icciusalis*, living among *Potamogeton natans*, a plant which together with the beautiful water fern, *Marsilia quadrifolia*, literally covers a portion of Fall Creek where it empties into Cayuga Lake, at Ithaca, N. Y.

The Field Station of Cornell University is located at this place. It is under the supervision of Dr. James G. Needham, and to him I owe my introduction to the water-loving caterpillars. It is a very large "red letter" that marks the day when, with this eminent scientist, I first found the insects and saw their natural habitat.

Dr. Needham located the place where he had previously taken Nymphulas, and with a dip-net began to sweep the surface vegetation for them. After each sweep, he would empty the contents of the net into a shallow tray, and hand them over for me to examine. I became so intensely interested in the myriad forms of aquatic life which were thus spread before me, that I neglected to search for the caterpillars, however, until Dr. Needham pointed out a specimen.

How fortunate for me that he knew the tricks of this larva, otherwise I might never have discovered it, for the caterpillar

Side view   Front view

Pupa of *Nymphula icciusalis* (three times life size)

lives concealed between two green leaf fragments that are held together by tiny silk stitches.

The first found case proved to be the largest of the twenty gathered, and, like the others, was made from two irregular pieces of leaf cut from Potamogeton.

In color the cases were so like the plants on which they rested, or to which they were attached, that it was difficult to locate them until they were dislodged by the net.

Upon reaching my room I placed the specimens in a wash-bowl of lake water with leaves of both Potamogeton and water fern. I did this in order to learn if the larvæ would make use of the latter plant.

Careful examination of several cases showed that the edges of the two pieces from which each case was made were stitched together along their sides but left free at the ends. These openings permitted a larva to thrust forth its head at will and to eject its excrement beyond the boundaries of its home.

The caterpillars were secured on July twenty-ninth. The following morning I found that all were upon the upper side of the leaves, and that a number of the insects had cut new roof pieces for their dwellings.

In order to learn how the cutting was done, I removed a larva from its case, and placed it upon a fresh, perfect leaf floating in a glass of water. As I did so I discovered that the caterpillar had become dry and somewhat shrunken during its exposure to the air.

When the larva realized that it was again in its natural element it lost no time in crawling to the under side of the leaf. As it entered the water a film of air seemed to envelop its body. Near the edge of the leaf it began to spin a slight web. Later I learned that this served to support the larva while it cut a fairly good parallelogram, three-fourths of an inch in length by one-third of an inch in width, from the leaf. Before the piece was entirely severed, I saw displayed what might be called caterpillar intelligence. The Nymphula left off cutting and began to rejoin the edges of the incision, catching them together with a few stitches of silk. Apparently it did this because the cut portion was be-

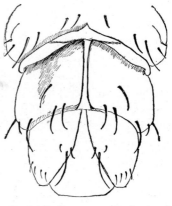

The bristle like setæ on the head and the first and second segments of *Nymphula icciusalis*

ginning to sag. This may have annoyed the larva or made the cutting more difficult. It took the caterpillar three hours in all to accomplish the work, then, with the newly acquired covering above its back, it travelled to the farther edge of the leaf and there began to snip out a floor foundation.

In studying the Nymphulas I observed that usually they did their cutting while resting on the under side of a leaf, and that the pieces of a case were alternately discarded, which explained why the two sides were rarely of equal freshness.

All of the cuttings were cleanly made; there was no after shaping, no change of line. I could easily find the leaf from which a new floor or roof had been taken, and replace the fragment so that it fitted the hole perfectly. While there was no uniformity in shape, the pieces were more or less oblong and somewhat elliptical. Judging by the number of leaf pieces which were always found floating upon the water in the morning the work of rebuilding must have been done largely at night.

A couple of days after I had placed the Nymphulas in the bowl, I found its sides blotched with dark specks, so I concluded that refuse matter in the water had been washed up while I was observing and handling the insects. I removed the plants and larvæ, cleaned the bowl, refilled it with fresh water, and replaced the specimens. The next morning I found that the bowl was in the same unsightly condition, and not only the bowl, but papers upon my desk where it stood were well sprinkled with dark stains.

Larva of *Nymphula icciusalis* (greatly enlarged)

I sat down and began to watch. In a very few moments a small pellet of excrement was landed on a note-book some four feet away. Looking in the direction from which it came, I saw a case on the farther side of the dish, with its long diameter pointing toward the book; undoubtedly its inmate had ejected the refuse. During the days that followed I was surprised at the force with which these small insects shot forth their pellets. Apparently it was the Nymphula way of keeping a clean house.

On August third the larvæ were without Potamogeton leaves until evening, when I gave them a fresh supply. It was then that I noticed two round holes in the edge of a water fern leaf. Probably the pieces had been taken for building pur-

Potamogeton natans leaf with pupa case one-fifth smaller than
life size attached to stem at *A*. A foundation piece being cut
out at *B*. Holes in a water fern leaf made by the larvæ at *C*

poses; but another leaf showed unmistakable evidence that
its tissue had been eaten. So far as I know, this was the
only time that the water fern was disturbed by the caterpillars.
The larva in the case first secured showed no inclination to

change its covering. By August fourth this had become a dull yellow, and I found that the edges of the upper and lower pieces had been joined for their entire length, but in such a way that a fair-sized space was left about the insect. Upon holding the case to the light I saw that its inmate had changed to the pupa state, so I deemed it wise to examine, under a microscope, some mature larvæ as well as others that were but partly grown. They did not differ greatly in appearance, and none showed any indication of tracheal filaments, or gills. To the naked eye the insects were just dull grayish-white caterpillars with shiny yellow heads and dimpled bodies which narrowed slightly from the middle to the ends. The lens revealed other markings, however, that are characteristic of this species of Nymphula.*

I am indebted to Dr. Harrison G. Dyar and Mr. W. D. Kearfott for the identification of this insect.

I found that the caterpillars did not remain submerged for any great length of time; but if removed from the water and left for several hours they showed plainly that they were out of their element.

In order to learn, if possible, how they breathed, I killed and dissected several specimens, but discovered nothing unusual in the tracheal system except that the breathing tubes were finely branched. I must own that I do not know how these caterpillars obtain their oxygen unless from air which they hold about their bodies by means of misroscopic hairs.

In some way, however, they "get on," for one after another of my specimens attached its case to a leaf or stem, stopped eating, closed the doors of its house, shed its skin, and turned into a pupa, like any well-behaved land-dwelling caterpillar.

* A more detailed and scientific description of the caterpillar will be found in Appendix A.

Two of the distinctive characteristics of the pupa are shown in the photographs—the ventral sheath, covering the tongue antennæ and legs, which extends beyond the end of the abdomen, and the three pairs of large, red, round spiracles, or breathing-holes.

During the evening of August twelfth I saw a little moth fly from the side of the bowl to the wall, directly under an

Nymphula icciusalis moth (about three times life size)

electric light. A few seconds later I placed the opened cyanide jar over the beautiful winged creature, and thus secured my first mature specimen of *Nymphula icciusalis*.

The moth had thread-like antennæ and a long tongue. Its abdomen was banded with light brown and cream-colored scales; the wings showed large areas of white and yellow-ochre, outlined in part by brown lines; the delicate fringes were spotted with very dark brown markings that can be easily traced in the accompanying photograph. These wings were deeply creased, as if they had been folded lengthwise. The legs had a light brown color; the pair nearest the head being the shortest, and without the double spurs of the other two pairs. The middle and hind legs were quite long for so small an insect, but no doubt they keep the delicate wings from coming in contact with the wet leaves of the water plants while the moth deposits her eggs.

This first adult came from a pupa that formed on August sixth, and when spread it measured less than three-fourths of an inch from tip to tip of its fore wings.

As other moths emerged, I learned that the males and females of this species are alike.

The only eggs which I saw were those deposited by a moth after she had been placed in a poison jar. They were very small and of a honey-yellow color.

I found no eggs in the open, although I searched diligently for them later, at a lake near my home in Ohio, and I saw no moths of this species upon the wing. However, they have been reported as flying from May nineteenth to September third.

When I learned that the early stages of *Nymphula icciusalis* had not been definitely known until I gathered the larvæ at Ithaca and carried them to maturity, I decided that two "red letters" were needed to mark properly that day when I first found this species of water-loving caterpillars.

CHAPTER XXI

A MOTH THAT DELIBERATELY POLLINATES
A PLANT

THE PRONUBA, *Pronuba yuccasella*

"It mounts! It flies! It seeks the skies;
 It flies from bloom to bloom!
E'en so, my soul, shalt thou arise
 Resurgent, from the tomb."

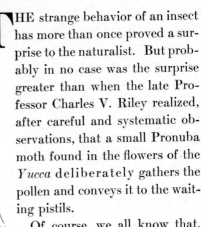

THE strange behavior of an insect has more than once proved a surprise to the naturalist. But probably in no case was the surprise greater than when the late Professor Charles V. Riley realized, after careful and systematic observations, that a small Pronuba moth found in the flowers of the *Yucca* deliberately gathers the pollen and conveys it to the waiting pistils.

Of course, we all know that, before a flower can perfect seed, its pollen or that of some other blossom must reach the stigma at the end of the pistil; and that whenever self-pollination is impossible because of the stamens and pistils occupying different flowers, maturing at different times, or being arranged so that the life-giving dust in the anthers at the end of the sta-

135

mens cannot reach the stigma, some outside agent comes to the assistance of the plant and helps to distribute its pollen; and that, in many cases, this service is performed by insects as they sip the nectar which the blossoms secrete. While feasting, they brush the pollen on to their bodies and either dust it upon the stigma when they depart or carry it to a neighboring flower which, in this way, is cross-fertilized.

That certain flowers have become specialized so that they yield their honey only to the insects that will serve them is also well understood. For example, there are the orchids, which are probably the most exacting of their kind, although many a wayside weed uses remarkable methods in order to secure the attention of the insect that will propagate its species. These nectar-loving guests, however, do not intentionally serve the blossoms which they frequent, their aid being purely incidental to their quest for food.

But the relationship existing between the genus *Yucca* and the small Pronuba moths has been found to be of an entirely different nature, for while the flowers offer little or no treat to the moths, the moths have mouth parts specially developed for collecting and distributing the plant's pollen. And, strange as it may seem, this is the only lepidopterous insect known to fertilize a blossom intentionally, its purpose being apparently to insure the development of *Yucca* seed in order that a portion of it may nourish the Pronuba caterpillars as they mature in the ovaries of the flowers.

By the merest chance, I learned of the interdependence of these insects and the plants which they visit, but it was a couple of years before I found *Yucca* growing in sufficient profusion to enable me to study their pollination carefully. Then early one spring I came upon a large bed of *Yucca filamentosa* in a city park. As the park was some distance from my home and

Photograph by King

A large bed of *Yucca filamentosa*

rather inaccessible, I did not revisit it until the twentieth of July, when I received a message from the head gardener— a most intelligent Scotchman whom I had interested in the subject—saying that the plants were in full bloom.

Photograph by King
Pronuba moth in the flower (two-thirds life size)

That afternoon, with an enthusiastic young naturalist friend and his camera, I went to the park, and along the water driveway saw thousands upon thousands of tall stalks of drooping white lilies. Each stalk was protected at the base by a great number of sword-like leaves which stood out stiffly and made it somewhat difficult to approach the flowers.

When we began to examine these, we found that the lower blossoms on a panicle were invariably faded, and that in many cases the seed-pods were well developed. Were we too late for the moths? If not, they should be found hiding within the lily bells.

The boy was the first to locate an insect. He held back the petals in order that I might determine if it were a Pronuba. It had the characteristic white satiny wings of the moth, but I was not absolutely certain of its identity until by the aid of a glass I saw a pellet of pollen under the head. Then I realized that we had before us—actually before us—the object of our search, and, deciding that a moth in sight is worth two in some undiscovered flower, we took its photograph. Such haste proved unnecessary, however, for within an hour we found at least a hundred of its species.

Occasionally we discovered two moths within the same blossom, and one of these usually proved to be a male who, no doubt, had "a wooing come." I was surprised to find that these tiny moths were not in the least afraid of us. One seldom changed its position when observed unless we actually prodded it. Then it would run to the other side of the pistil or possibly into a neighboring flower, but rarely sought safety in flight. Did the small creature understand through inherited knowledge that its close resemblance in color to the petals made it inconspicuous? Probably this was the case, for protective coloration is not unusual among animals, and under ordinary circumstances it proves most effective.

Photograph by King　　　*Courtesy " Country Life in America "*

Moth with pellet of pollen under her head
(Microscopic photograph)

With a powerful lens we examined many specimens of the Pronuba and found that the males were never laden with pollen, and for a very good reason: they lacked the necessary organs for carrying it; but a Madam Pronuba usually held a ball of the yellow dust at her neck, using for the purpose a pair of clasping organs, or palpi, attached to the lower side of her head, and another pair of organs, the palpi maxillæ, located on either side of her tongue. At the base of each palpus maxillæ there was seen the tentacle which has been so peculiarly developed in this genus of moth for the purpose of gathering and disposing of the Yucca's pollen.

These tentacles were very flexible and in form resembled a Liliputian pair of ram's horns. Their surfaces were covered with minute hairs and small tubercles set with spines, and these must assist greatly in keeping the pollen grains together.

The many-jointed antennæ, the noses of the moth, so to speak, as well as its head, body, and upper wings, were clothed with white scales. The black eyes were very noticeable against this whiteness, and so were the dusky under wings and tip of the ovipositor when they came in view.

The tongue of a moth or butterfly is in reality its jaws drawn out into a tube for sucking purposes; but in some species the two halves of the tube are not exactly fitted to each other, and when this occurs the insect cannot feed. Apparently this is the case with *Pronuba yuccasella*, for we found that the tongues of several specimens were disconnected for a short space above their tips, and we did not observe the moths searching about the base of a pistil where the nectar glands, still present in the flower, open, and where honey at some time in the history of the plant must have been secreted.

At about half-past seven the Pronubas began to fly from one panicle of flowers to another, which indicated that they were collecting and distributing pollen. With the light from our

bull's-eye lantern turned into a blossom it was not difficult
to see the moth when present, and we had located and observed
at least a dozen before we saw one run up a stamen and stop
with her head above its extremity; we held our breath. Would
she or would she not—that was the question. Suddenly she
threw her long tongue and her palpi maxillæ out over the
anther and scraped the pollen from it toward her tentacles.
She then packed this upon the mass she already carried, and
while her movements were so rapid that I could not follow
them in detail, it seemed as if she used both her front feet and
her tentacles to shape and adjust the load.

In the briefest space of time the moth was at work on a
second anther, when, either because the light annoyed her or
possibly in order to dispose of the pollen which she had gathered, she curled her tentacles about the mass and flew from the
flower into the darkness.

The boy and I each took a deep breath. We had seen an
insect intentionally perform a task and with tools given her
for the purpose.

Later observations of moths at work among flowers which I
kept fresh in water at home proved the correctness of my
impressions as to the way in which the Pronubas accumulate
the pollen grains.

I can never forget the feeling of awe and wonder that swept
over me when on turning back the petals of a flower I discovered a moth in the act of fertilizing the pistil. She held
the style firmly between her spurred legs with her head just
above its extremity, and she moved her tentacles in and out
of the stigmatic chamber with rapid, jerky motions which literally jammed the pollen into the opening. Then when the
work had been satisfactorily accomplished she turned, ran
down the pistil, turned again, and began to search over the

walls of the ovary. Her movements indicated plainly that she was in quest of something, and that something proved to be a place in which to oviposit. After a deal of fussing she settled her wee body between two of the stamens and a second later reared the end of her abdomen, thrust a long ovipositor into the walls of the pistil, and deposited an egg among its embryo seeds. Back to the stigma she went with more pollen, returned to her position on the pistil, and this time laid two eggs before she again fertilized the flower. Then she flew into a neighboring blossom, and I noticed that her load of pollen was diminished in size.

I tried to follow the movements of this Pronuba, but she had evidently become annoyed by our presence and soon eluded us.

What dainty, busy little moth mothers they were, and how intent upon their own affairs! As a rule, they laid one or more eggs in the pistil of a freshly opened flower before they pollenized it, but occasionally the programme was reversed. A moth rarely placed more than six eggs in a pistil, however, and this might be taken as an indication that she did not wish to over-tax the fruit of the plant which was to serve as "board and bed" for her future children.

It is possible that these Pronubas slyly gather pollen during the day, although I have never seen them at work until dusk. If this is not the case, they must retain a portion of what they secure at night for future distribution, for a female moth is seldom found in hiding without her yellow load.

My observations of this species of Pronuba lead me to believe that the *Yucca filamentosa* is propagated by cross-fertilization, for only once have I seen a moth go from the anther to the pistil of the same flower, and then I was not certain that she collected pollen.

Seed pods of *Yucca filamentosa*

The genus *Yucca* covers a great portion of our country, and the plants range in size from *Yucca filamentosa*, common in our Eastern gardens, to *Yucca arborescens*, or Joshua tree, of the South-west, and each variety of the genus, with possibly one exception, is practically and peculiarly dependent for fructification upon some species of the Pronuba moth. When the moth is absent, Yuccas seldom produce seed even if visited by other insects, and a careful investigation of this fact shows that in order to fertilize the pistil the pollen must be thrust well into its stigmatic opening, a service which the chance visitor cannot perform, so Dame Nature in the long ago modified the mouth-parts of the female Pronubas for the work, and although the moths are not directly recompensed for their labor, they realize in some way that in serving the plant they are providing food for their children and are content to do without the nectar which tempts many an insect into a blossom that in consequence of the visit becomes fertilized.

These Pronubas do their work well, for ten days after we had watched them pollenate certain flowers we found the seed-pods developing, and with the aid of a microscope discovered the merest specks of caterpillars living cosily within the growths.

When the pods were nearly formed I removed several of the stalks to my porch and placed them in water. The fruit did not wither but continued to develop, and each pod showed by its constricted appearance where larvæ were feeding within.

On the twenty-second of August I examined a number of these pods and found that in some the caterpillars appeared to be of the same age, while in others they varied in size as well as color. I did not see any of the larvæ cast their skins, but the little fellows were white, the larger ones pink, and later the mature caterpillars, measuring a half-inch in length, assumed a deep rose color. All had dark heads and light feet, and they travelled quite rapidly although they lacked the pro-legs which usually support the long body of a caterpillar, and, in consequence, they were slug-like in form.

After the first of September I began to notice small round openings in the sides of the pods. I knew that each was the exit through which an imprisoned cater-pillar had crawled, but, watch as I would, I could not discover a larva in the act of departing. Finally it dawned upon me that the insects must be leaving at night, for each morning there would be several freshly cut doorways.

As I wished to secure a few of the crawlers, I cut the upper portion from a seed-stalk and placed the fruit in a large jar which I then closed. In this way I captured a few of the insects and placed them on a leaf-strewn box of earth, where they soon disappeared.

On the thirteenth of September in broad daylight one rose-red caterpillar proved an exception to the rule. At least, I found it swinging by the finest of

Small round openings in the sides of the pods

silken threads which it spun for the purpose as it descended from the seed-pod. A clever little acrobat, surely, that on reaching the bottom of the jar squirmed and wriggled over the smooth surface with an instinctive desire to bury itself according to the prescribed rules of the family. What a brief bit of out-of-door existence these caterpillars have! It is just long enough to enable them to go from their green cradles to a resting-place in the ground.

A week after the last Pronuba of my colony had "gone be-

When the first flowers of *Yucca filamentosa* open

low," I scraped the leaves from the earth and ploughed this up with a pencil in order to find if the larvæ had made their cocoons. Yes, there they were, little silken blankets, which each insect had woven and wrapped about its body before lying down to await its transformation—a transformation which, unlike that of most silk-spinning caterpillars, does not occur until long after the cocoons are finished. In fact, these insects change to the pupa or dormant state only a short time before *Yucca filamentosa* blooms.

But when the first flowers open, some inherited impulse causes the insects to break through their pupa-cases, discard their cocoon wrappings, and emerge as little white moths. They find that their wings are damp and undeveloped, however, so until these have become inflated and strong, the Pronubas cling to the leaves of the Yuccas. But, at length, with a glad flutter they go forth into the dusk to do the work assigned to them in the great plan of nature.

CHAPTER XXII

THE PEST OF THE WOODBINE

The Eight-Spotted Forester, *Alypia octomaculata*

"Some in richest and softest of velvets arrayed,
Or in mail that does shame to the armorer's trade."

I HAD spent the summer at an old gray farm-house whose weather-beaten boards showed the ravages of years, especially at the corner of the porch where a leaky spout had made the floor quite rotten. The porch was cool and shady during the hot days, for it was well protected by vines of woodbine and wild clematis, and I had found it a particularly pleasant nook from which to watch the birds and butterflies that frequented the orchard and the old-fashioned garden.

I also had the opportunity of studying the development of some brown-banded caterpillars that had been rather numerous upon the woodbine, and which I had induced my hostess to leave unmolested for my benefit and the benefit of the English sparrows that frequently breakfasted upon them. These insects had appeared early in May and again in August, but it was not until September third that I learned how they prepare for their pupa state.

148

I was trying to sew on the porch that morning, but the day was so fine I could only dream and enjoy the fragrance of the late flowers.

Suddenly I realized that a fully grown brown larva was moving laboriously across the porch floor. From experience, I knew that many crawlers, when ready to give up their creeping existence, "go below," so I concluded that this "pest of the woodbine," commonly known as the Eight-spotted Forester, was taking its last journey.

The caterpillar went toward that part of the porch

Photograph by King

The brown-banded caterpillars of the woodbine

where the boards were decayed, and it occurred to me that it would have reached the earth in a much shorter time had it travelled in an opposite direction; however, I gave the matter no special thought until the insect stopped at the rotten boards and began to nose about as if searching for something. I then drew close to his wormship, and with a glass watched every movement. At first I believed that the caterpillar had mistaken the soft wood for mother earth, and that when it realized the fact it would go on to the ground; but I soon found that no mistake was being made, for after a short delay the Forester began to cut into the wood with its jaws. In went the head,

The little moths with eight lemon disks
on their black velvet wings

farther and farther, and as the work progressed a miniature pile of sawdust accumulated at one side of the excavation. Down went the larva until it was entirely concealed. Then it turned about and, with jaws close to the opening, spun silken threads from its small spinneret and wove these into a curtain which it stretched across the door-way.

It was a wise caterpillar, however, for it knew that such a conspicuous covering was undesirable, so it wove the sawdust in with the silk, and when the task was finished the sharpest of eyes could scarcely discover the aperture through which, later, a gay little moth, with eight lemon disks on its black velvet wings, and orange knee-breeches beneath, would emerge.

Most of us who have woodbine or grapes about our houses know this day-flying moth, but very few realize that the insect is responsible for the brown-banded caterpillar upon these vines.

CHAPTER XXIII

A "PUSS" CATERPILLAR

Cerura cinerea

"Feeble though the insect be,
Allah speaks through that to thee!"

YEARS ago I read an article in a magazine about a queer "Puss" caterpillar, *Dicranura vinula*. The story was written by Dr. Wm. M. Wheeler, and it was told in the same interesting manner that Dr. Wheeler employs to-day in describing our ant neighbors. When I had finished his account of the insect I had a great desire to know it personally, but as it is a foreign species, I could not hope to find it in America, so I began a search for native larvæ with similar characteristics.

About the middle of August I found one resting on a silken mat spread upon the upper surface of a willow leaf. Dr. Harrison G. Dyar identified it as *Cerura cinerea.*

The willow shaded a watering-trough on a country road, and because Dolly, our horse, was thirsty, I discovered the specimen. When I placed it in a collecting box a fly not unlike a small house-fly flew from its back.

In consequence of this parasite's visit the "Puss" failed to become a moth. Instead it was obliged to nourish the fly's

Larvæ of "Puss" moth
(two-thirds life size)

larvæ until they developed into four brown pupæ that could be seen through the skin of the depleted caterpillar.

The next year and the next and still the next I found these "Puss" caterpillars, some small and some fully grown, but several seasons passed before I secured eggs, and then six came from my Vinton friend.

All were laid singly on the under side of aspen leaves and, with one exception, at the extreme tip of the leaf. They were domeshaped, of a rich dark red-brown color, and had a leathery surface.

These eggs began to hatch on June twenty-ninth, and the shells were not eaten by the larvæ, which emerged through openings on the sides.

At birth the head of the young caterpillar is large, out of all proportion to the size of its body, and this size is accentuated because on the first segment of the thorax there is a pair of appendages that stand out and simulate pricked-up ears. The head and upper portion of the body are a light madder-red that soon deepens in tone, but the under surface, including the feet and prolegs, remains pale buff. On the back over the third and fourth segments and again over the fifth, sixth, and seventh segments there are two oval greenish patches, while the dark anal claspers, drawn out into long tails, are encircled by three yellow bands. These tails are flexible whips and each holds a concealed lash. When the caterpillar is frightened or annoyed it rears and spreads the tails, and then shooting out the lashes it waves them about in a most threatening manner. It has been reported that a liquid, supposedly of an injurious nature, is yielded from these lashes, but I have never been able to detect the least sign of it.

Head of young caterpillar
(greatly enlarged)

The young larvæ drank eagerly and at first ate only the soft cellular tissue from the under side of the leaf, but the following day they ate holes through the leaf's surface.

The little crawlers deserve the name of "Puss" caterpillars, for they resemble a cat not only in the shape of the head but also in their kittenish ways; especially was this true when two or three came together.

They were good natured and easy to rear because they ate not only leaves of aspen but those of such common trees as willow and poplar.

The family that I had under observation showed that they were preparing to moult on July the third, and three days later all were out in fresh skins.

The larvæ seemed much as before except that another green spot had appeared on the back of each.

The caterpillars ate little and grew slowly, moulting for the second time between the eighth and the eleventh.

After this the tails of one caterpillar gradually shortened until by July fifteenth they had become two small horns in appearance.

The insect, to my knowledge, did not cast its skin again until the twenty-first, although it remained on a moulting mat for four days. When the redressing was accomplished, however, "Puss" made up for lost time by appearing in the guise of the final moult.

The larva was very striking in its clear green skin and elaborately wrought saddle-patch of brown, edged and ornamented in yellow. The saddle extended from the third to the eleventh segment where the color continued on to the tips of the spined tails. The head remained dark and a triangle of this brown on the thorax gave a hooded appearance to the face.

This larva ate ravenously for three days, then within twenty-four hours the dark madder-brown began to fade from its back and seemingly to run down into the green sides, which in consequence became a dirty pink.

Realizing that the caterpillar was nearing the pupa state, I confined it with a piece of old gray wood, and on the smooth cut end of this it immediately began to spin. The caterpillar rested with its body curved sidewise, and as it spun, it slowly reversed its position so that all portions of the thickening walls came easily in contact with the little spinnerette. The cocoon grew tough like parchment and gray like the wood, and to all outward appearances was completed in one hour and a half.

Photograph by Bash

Two cocoons spun on old wood

Cocoons spun the previous year in a brown pasteboard box

had been of light brown rather than of a gray color. Might not this indicate that the "Puss" larva is conscious of its color surroundings when it pupates for its long winter sleep?

The "Puss" moth, *Cerura cinerea*

Another "Puss" passed its final moult on July twenty-fifth and fed till the thirty-first. The following day it lost its brilliant color and spun a cocoon close to that of the first pupating caterpillar.

This larva lived six days longer than its fellow, but it did not acquire so great a size, although it was kept supplied with plenty of food.

Disaster overtook the four remaining caterpillars before they reached the pupa period, and again I despaired of completing the life history of the insect. But in August both cocoons yielded perfect adults and, best of all, the smaller larva proved to be a male and the larger a female.

The gray moths with their light under wings and a brown patch on the thoraces are not nearly so pretty as the "Puss" caterpillars, and the insects would be quite uninteresting were it not for the eccentricities of their larval existence.

CHAPTER XXIV

YOUNG ARCHITECTS

The Basilarchias, *Basilarchia*

"And what's a butterfly, at best?
'Tis but a caterpillar dressed."

THE Promethea is not the only caterpillar that realizes the necessity of strengthening the petiole of the leaf in which it builds its winter home. The fall brood of Basilarchia butterflies secure their small domiciles or hibernacula in much the same way and for the same reason; that is, to prevent them from falling when the leaves become detached. I have seen the insects at work as early as the fifteenth of August and from that on until late in October.

After a larva has selected a leaf for its home it begins by winding the petiole with silk and attaching this to the twig much as does the Promethea. But, unlike that insect, the Basilarchia cuts and snips away its leaf until the portion near the base becomes a very irregular and much elongated diamond. It then lines this with silk and by connecting the edges

156

gradually rolls it about its body. It does this with infinite care, however, going in and out many times before the interior is finished to its satisfaction.

One feature of the house is its balcony, the projecting end of the midvein, and here on a fine fall day the caterpillar is often seen taking a sun bath. But when cold weather arrives a Basilarchia crawls into its snuggery and closes the door with a little tuft of bristles which grow on the end of

The hibernaculum

A Basilarchia cuts and snips away the leaf

its body, and thus it hibernates. I have always found it to be a late sleeper, but it has been seen eating the "pussies" before the leaves were open.

One spring I accidentally discovered a dozen or fifteen of the hibernacula upon a young poplar. A number of the inmates appeared, but others remained in seclusion and these I prodded out, but they resented my interference and, like sulky children, each kept its face close to the twig on which it clung and for days refused to eat. I do not believe that any of the disturbed larvæ lived to become pupæ, so there may be some law beyond human understanding which governs the going-out and coming-in of a caterpillar.

One feature of the house is its balcony

There are several species of *Basilarchia*, and they feed upon a variety of plants; but in my locality I find only the *Basilarchia astyanax* and *Basilarchia disippus*, commonly called the Red-spotted Purple and the Viceroy, and these are usually upon poplar and willow.

There are two, and in some cases three, generations of the Basilarchias each year, and, strange as it may seem, those of the spring and early summer never show any inclination to make leaf-shelters, but live exposed, although they use other protective devices and disguises of their race.

The eggs of these insects are invariably found at the extreme tip of the leaf, and here, when the little crawler emerges, it begins to feed and in such a manner that the midvein is denuded for a short space. This is then stiffened with wrappings of silk and bits of leaf in order, as Dr. Scudder suggests, to prevent its curling and shrivelling. We find that the young crawler rests upon this support during the day—being a night feeder—and is quite inconspicuous, especially after it has made and hung up a small bundle of rubbish. Of course, the real

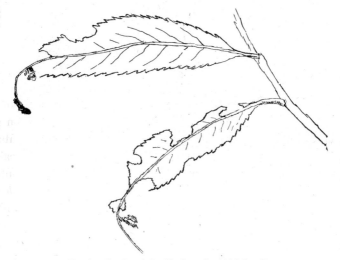

Showing the denuded midvein and rubbish bundles

use of this dangling package is problematic, but as in nature a moving object is more noticeable than one at rest, it is likely that the swaying bundle diverts the attention of the bird or insect from the caterpillar whose presence it has located, for we find that every young Viceroy and Red-spotted Purple, in the open, considers such a package essential to its well-being, and that when one is snipped off by an enemy another soon swings in its place.

After a caterpillar has moulted for the second time, it deserts the midvein of the leaf which can no longer support its

It actually flaunts its ugly humps and bumps upon the surface of the leaf where it feeds (one-half life size)

weight, and travels to the petiole or to a near-by twig where it rests during the day. But as it increases in size it assumes such an irregular and repulsive appearance that it no longer seeks concealment, but instead actually flaunts its ugly humps and bumps upon the surface of the leaf where it feeds.

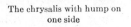

The Red-spotted Purple and Viceroy caterpillars are very similar and, when mature, their colors are arranged so that the insects resemble bird excrement, a device serviceable to them, no doubt, at this period of their existence.

But when ready to discard the last larva skin, they, like all cater-

The chrysalis with hump on one side

160

pillars, lose their vivid colors and become faded. It is then that each makes a journey to some seemingly safe retreat and there weaves a silken carpet upon a convenient support, in the meshes of which it fastens the claspers at the end of its

Upper—Viceroy butterfly. Lower—Red-spotted Purple butterfly (smaller than life size)

body, and deliberately holds by these claspers, head down, until an irregular closed box, the chrysalis, emerges from the ruptured skin. As it does this a strange thing happens, for while the skin still partially envelops the chrysalis, the chrysalis stretches up and inserts the cremaster at its caudal extremity into the meshes, and in so doing insures its safety before

Monarch butterflies, of which the Viceroy has become a close copy

the discarded skin relaxes its hold. And it does this although it resembles nothing so much as an irregular closed box with a great hump on one side.

The transformation of a butterfly, as you see, is not carried on within a cocoon or cell like that of a moth, but in the open;

Photograph by King

The gay little masquerader

and when we find a Basilarchia chrysalis with a very dark color we may be certain that the enfolded butterfly is about to appear. But before it does this, it must lift the portion just above its face, and so open a passage into the world. But the butterfly when it emerges is not ready for flight. Like the moths, it must preen and dry its feathers, distend its wings and strengthen them before it can go forth into the sunshine.

The Red-spotted Purple butterfly still wears the dark dress of its kind although there is a shimmer of iridescent blue upon the upper surface of its wings and a bit of Persian embroidery beneath. Its first cousin, the Viceroy, through natural selection has become a close copy of the Monarch butterfly, of an entirely different genus. It, like the Antiopa, is a gay little masquerader. But does it wear the borrowed plumes of orange and black for a purpose? Possibly, if the "wise men" are correct in their supposition that the Monarch is unpalatable and therefore immune from the birds.

CHAPTER XXV

A GAY MASQUERADER

The Antiopa, *Vanessa antiopa*

"Zigzag butterflies, many a pair,
  Doubled and danced in the sunny air."

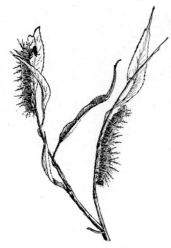

ONE of the first butterflies to greet us in the spring is the *Vanessa antiopa* or Mourning Cloak, a gay masquerader that is forever misleading and deceiving us with its antics. Many of us while gathering early flowers have noticed this black butterfly with a yellow edge and a border of violet spots upon its wings; once in March I counted thirty specimens feasting on the sap of a maple tree. Where did they come from? Well, the Antiopa is a butterfly that hibernates in the winter, that is, it goes to sleep, or at least remains dormant during the greater part of the cold weather.

It must nap with one eye open, however, for it has been reported as seen on the wing in every month of the year and practically in every part of the world. Its numbers and wide distribution are due in part to the fact that it is a species protected by mimicry. Now, we all know that a mimic imitates some one or some thing, and the Antiopa when it alights upon the bark of a tree, as it frequently does, or among dead leaves or rubbish upon the ground, closes its wings above the back in true butterfly style, and at once becomes inconspicuous, because the under surface of the wings is mottled and colored in

One of the first butterflies to greet us in the spring

such a way that they simulate the surrounding background. Of course, it is not likely that this butterfly realizes in the least that it is masquerading, but it does realize that such a resting-place offers safety; and possibly it realizes that in order to secure the greatest degree of protection, it must remain motionless while danger threatens. Some scientists believe that this habit of keeping quiet when startled or attacked, a fixed characteristic of the Antiopa, is the result of fear, a kind of paralysis, for the insect at such times can be picked up by a leg or thrown upon the floor without its showing the least sign of life. I have seen a specimen sham death, to all appearances, for five minutes while it lay, a most conspicuous object, on my hand.

The butterflies of this species which have survived the winter begin to oviposit when the leaf-buds are ready to open. They place their seven or eight-sided eggs so that they encircle a twig, usually of willow, poplar, or elm, and two weeks later the caterpillars emerge and find fresh food for their snipping. At birth they have warm yellow-brown bodies, much spined, and large dark heads. The little crawlers live as a colony on the under side of a leaf, and not only are they gregarious in their early life but this habit is retained during their entire larval existence. They move rapidly, and as they go each spins a silken thread; these threads become veritable suspension bridges and facilitate the progress of the insects from one twig to another.

The mature larvæ of the *Vanessa antiopa* are two and one-half inches in length. Their bodies are black, frosted with white, and each has a dorsal row of eight red spots and red pro-

The mature larvæ are two and one-half inches in length

legs; while, as with all of the genus, the surface of the skin is well protected by branched spines.

When ready to change into the pupa state, the caterpillar stops eating, spins a little rosette of silk, fastens into this its last pair of prolegs, and for twenty-four hours hangs thus, head down and very quiet. Ah, but "still waters run deep," and unfathomable changes are taking place within that limp, helpless body.

The skin cracks at the head and wrinkles back and off from the emerging chrysalis

Just what occurs at this time in the breaking down or building up of the anatomy of the insect is not fully understood, but, by and by, there is a spasmodic twitching, and the skin cracks at the head and wrinkles back and off from the emerging chrysalis.

Caterpillar ready to change to the pupa state

This feat is not always successfully performed; sometimes an insect is unable to free itself from the black dress and is caught in its own "headgear," or possibly if it fails to fasten the hook at the end of its body into the rosette of silk, it falls to the ground, and there must take its chance of surviving the chrysalis period of three weeks.

If no accident has occurred, however, the irregular shell of violet-

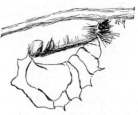

The insect is sometimes caught in its own "headgear"

brown hangs secure, and one can see how snugly the future butterfly is tucked away within.

I have found the butterflies from these spring chrysalides

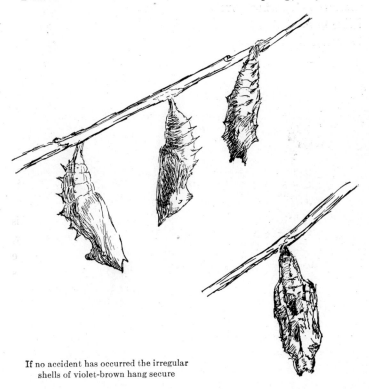

If no accident has occurred the irregular
shells of violet-brown hang secure

early in July, and their eggs from then on into August, for the insect is double-brooded.

It is one of the species which after leaving the chrysalis voids a red liquid. If the butterflies are sufficiently common in any place the spots left by them are responsible for the phenomenon known in olden days as the rain of blood.

The Antiopa may be kept as a pet during the winter, for it is hardy and will sip decaying fruit and sweetened water.

There is a pretty story told of how the male butterfly emits musical notes when courting. I have never heard them, but I like to think it is because my ears are not sufficiently attuned to such delicate sounds, and that Sir Knight does go serenading his lady-love.

CHAPTER XXVI

DOOR–STEP NEIGHBORS

Children of the Painted Lady, *Pyrameis cardui*

"I'd be a butterfly born in a bower."

I FIND that first experiences with insects are indelibly recorded among my mental notes, and that whenever such an experience has proved especially pleasurable, it stands out like the initial letter of an illumined manuscript.

Probably no incident of the kind ever caused or ever will cause the delight which I felt in the early days of my insect work when I discovered the caterpillars of the Painted Lady butterfly, *Pyrameis cardui*, on hollyhock leaves at my very door.

Each caterpillar was perfectly hidden by a leaf whose edges were drawn together and fastened with silk. But the number of peculiarly rolled leaves attracted my attention and caused me to investigate, with the result that I found for the first time the Painted Lady's children. They were fully grown, being

Each caterpillar was perfectly hidden by a leaf whose edges were drawn
together and fastened with silk

an inch and a quarter in length, and had velvety black **bodies** with yellow side markings that were studded with wee tubercles out of which grew a few light hairs. These tubercles, under the glass, appeared to be rubies, garnets, and pearls sewed, as it were, upon a yellow ribbon for the purpose of holding it in place. Never since that day have I found Painted Lady caterpillars except on the thistle, where each dwells and frequently pupates in a fairy bower made from silken threads interwoven with the

Painted Lady caterpillar

downy seed plumes of the plant, and never since then have I seen the crawlers so brilliantly marked.

Later that summer I carried home what I believed to be the larvæ of this butterfly—caterpillars with hairy tubercles and similarly colored bodies. They were feeding upon willow, and while the butterfly books said nothing about willow as a food plant for the insect, neither did they say anything about hollyhock, so I was more than surprised when one of the willow "worms" began to bite pieces from the net covering of its box and with silk fashion them into a dense cocoon. Later it reappeared as a small, unattractive moth. When the opportunity came, I compared the butterfly and moth larvæ and saw how very dissimilar they are. This experience taught me the importance of making careful observations.

But to return to the hollyhocks "a-blooming at the door."

A Painted Lady caterpillar hanging ready to pupate in its bower upon the thistle and a suspended chrysalis

The eggs of the butterfly mother must have been deposited upon adjoining leaves, for the caterpillars, when I discovered them, were living close together, and the ragged appearance of the food plant proved that they had been in that neighborhood from the beginning.

174

I found the larvæ on June twenty-fifth and stood guard over them while a member of the family brought the glass jar in which they were to be housed.

Two days later when I removed its cover in order to change the food leaves, I saw that there were two chrysalides attached to its lower surface—beautiful things, which suggested, as they hung side by side, a pair of exquisite old-fashioned "earbobs." They were of a light brownish-violet color ornamented here and there with gold, as if Dame Nature had dipped her paint brush in the noonday sun and lightly touched their surfaces.

They hung together like a pair of old-fashioned "ear-bobs"

Having learned by experience how caterpillars in confinement disturb the helpless pupæ, I placed the lid holding those of the Painted Ladies over an empty jar and later added a twig of leaves to serve as a perch for the butterflies when they emerged. This occurred on the seventh of July. Both chrysalides opening within an hour of each other.

There are bronze-brown scales on the wings of *Pyrameis cardui* butterflies close to the body, and these merge into black toward the edge of the fore wings and into a tawny yellow-brown on the hind wings. There are white blotches in the black and irregular yellow-red markings on the fore wings, while near the margins of the hind wings there is a row of dark spots. On the under surface, these spots become eyes, and their number and size determine whether your specimen be a Painted Lady or her next of kin, the Painted Beauty, *Pyrameis huntera.*

The under surface of the Painted Lady's wings are marbled

Pyrameis cardui butterfly

in grays and browns, but across the fore wings there is a dash of rose, lemon, and black, usually concealed, however, by the overlapping hind wings.

It has been suggested that these "beauty spots" may attract or please the mate. Judging butterfly taste by our own, the

Painted Beauty caterpillar amid the flower-heads of the white and aromatic
everlasting

device should prove effective, for when one of these airy creatures alights upon the gray bark of a tree and waves its wings so that we catch an occasional glimpse of the rose, lemon, and black we are charmed by the butterfly and its coloring.

According to Dr. Scudder, these insects migrate in swarms and have been seen six hundred miles from land. In the South they remain upon the wing during the winter, but at the North they hibernate like the Antiopas, and do not reappear until May.

The Painted Beauty, however, either hibernates or passes the winter in the chrysalis form.

But no matter how or where the parents spend the cold weather, we are certain to find their children from June on into the Fall, those of the Painted Lady in bowers among the thistle leaves, and those of the Painted Beauty in equally dainty dwellings spun amid the flower-heads of the white and aromatic everlasting, *Graphalium.**

* Since this article was written I have reared Painted Lady butterflies from eggs found upon low mallow, *Malva rotundifolia.*

CHAPTER XXVII

ORCHARD VISITORS

The Angle-Wings or Graptas, *Grapta*

"Fluttering like some vain painted butterfly
From glade to glade along the forest path."

IF you are so fortunate as to visit an apple or peach orchard when the fruit is ripe, you will, in all probability, notice that some coppery-red butterflies, blotched and bordered with brown, are there before you. These butterflies are the Graptas, but we sometimes call them Angle-wings, because, as one entomologist says, they "look as if Mother Nature had with her scissors snipped the edges of their wings, fashioning notches and points according to the vagaries of an idle mood."

The Angle-wings like ourselves go to the orchards for fruit, and, if the truth be told, they prefer theirs overly ripe, actually in a fermented condition.

A number of these butterflies will gather on a rotting apple and take their tipple, becoming so absorbed in the treat that

179

They are often seen upon the leaves of hop

they are oblivious to danger and can be lifted between thumb and finger. Until they have reached this state, however, they resent any interference with their pleasure by flying at and about you with rapid zigzag movements. But frequently one alights upon a surface which is so similar to the gray-brown colors on the under side of its lifted wings that for the time the butterfly vanishes from sight as if by magic.

Possibly these tipplers, like our forefathers, believe that an apple or peach toddy is conducive to a good night's rest, and so drink deeply before retiring to some sheltered nook for their long hibernating sleep.

Chrysalis decked with rows of silver or gold spots

Early in the spring the Angle-wings reappear, and we see them drinking the sap of wounded trees and later the nectar of flowers. They are often found upon the leaves of hop, elm, nettle, hackberry, currant, and gooseberry, for it is on such trees and plants that their eggs are laid.

Several species of these butterflies deposit their eggs in short chains that hang from the under side of leaves like strings of beads. The "beads" are green, ornamented with vertical ridges, and each is shaped like a tiny barrel.

Dr. Scudder tells us that the eggs of one Grapta, the Hop-merchant, or *Grapta comma*, are deposited in this way, and that the last egg laid, which is placed at the summit of the column, is the first one to hatch.

The larva of the Hop-merchant when partly grown becomes

Each Grapta carries a distinguishing hall-mark in silver on the under side of its hind wings

a tent maker, for it bites the veins of a leaf in such a manner that the leaf droops and forms a room, and in this the young caterpillar lives in comparative safety.

The name Hop-merchant was given to these insects because during certain years it has done much toward harvesting the crop in hop vineyards.

Its brown chrysalis is angular and decked with rows of gold or silver spots.

The butterfly changes in appearance somewhat with the advance of the season; the upper surface of its wings becoming less heavily marked with brown, and the under surface losing much of its yellow tone.

Another Grapta, much like the Hop-merchant in color and markings but of a larger size, is the Violet-tip, *Grapta interrogationis*. It is also a dimorphic species but may be

A Grapta caterpillar (enlarged to show spines)

easily recognized among the others of the genus by its violet border and by the silver crescent and dot on the under surface of its hind wings. For this is the name plate of the Violet-tip butterfly, just as the letter C or G is the name plate of the Hop-merchant. In fact, each Grapta carries a distinguishing hall-mark in silver on the under side of its hind wings, and this helps greatly in the identification of a specimen.

My acquaintance with the Graptas began when I found two caterpillars, each one and a half inches long, feeding upon a hop vine. The crawlers were reddish-brown with light markings, and well protected with branched spines, which ranged in color from pale yellow to black. On July second both larvæ became chrysalides, and ten days later the butterflies emerged, and proved to be Violet-tips, but to my surprise they were quite dissimilar.

The mystery of this variation was not made clear to me until I read how this Violet-tip butterfly appears in two forms, and that while these forms are usually seasonal they are not of necessity so. It had chanced that one larva from the hop vine had assumed the colors and markings of the winter form while the other had retained the characteristics which distinguish it as the summer butterfly.

CHAPTER XXVIII

THE MONARCH

The Milkweed Butterfly, *Anosia plexippus*

"Lo, the bright train their radiant wings unfold!
With silver fringed, and freckled o'er with gold."

A LONE stalk of milkweed grew in our orchard. How it had escaped the browsing teeth of Dolly or the scythe of Cousin Joe was a mystery. But straight and beautiful it stood, its tumble of pink flowers swinging in the wind. One day I noticed a large tawny-and-black butterfly lazily approach and alight upon its blossoming surface. I knew that this beautiful creature, on account of its regal flight, was called *Anosia plexippus*, or the Monarch. Alas! my net missed the butterfly by the breadth of its wings. However, in the end, the loss was my gain, for what did I see but a tiny egg, a mere dot, upon the under side of a leaf! I held my breath, fearing that it might prove only a drop of the

185

One day I noticed a large tawny-and-black butterfly approach and alight
upon its blossoming surface

weed's milk, but no such disappointment was in store for me;
the glass showed plainly a very small cone with rows of pits,
separated by bands, upon its surface.

This was the first time that I had ever seen, with eyes that
could see, the egg of a butterfly. I marked down that day,
June thirtieth, therefore, as a red letter day of the summer.

I watched this egg and others found upon the plant until they
hatched into caterpillars, then I placed the little crawlers with
their food leaves in a breeding cage, and here they ate and grew
and cast their skins after the manner of their kind.

The Monarch larva is banded with black and white, and
later with yellow. As it becomes full grown four long black,
flexible horns develop, two of which project forward from the
front of the body and two backward from the caudal extremity.
When an insect is disturbed it waves these horns rapidly, as
if to show its displeasure.

THE MONARCH

Many people driving over a country road or walking through fields have noticed the larva of this Monarch butterfly feeding upon the milkweed, but I must own, to my shame, that never before had I been conscious of the caterpillars.

A day came when the clear, clean color of the larva hatched from the first egg found in the orchard grew faded. Having had little experience with insects at the time, I questioned, "Will it die?" It did not; instead, it prepared for and passed into the pupa form. On July seventeenth a gold-dotted chrysalis of an exquisite robin's-egg blue hung suspended where the caterpillar had been.

In this daintiest of all chrysalides the insect rested for

The larva of the Monarch butterfly feeding upon milkweed

eighteen days, then came its resurrection. But before the butterfly emerged I could see the color and markings of its wings.

Although these Monarchs fly with a slow, graceful motion, they are seldom attacked by birds, presumably because of some disagreeable quality which makes them unpalatable. Such a protective characteristic would surely lessen the dangers to which they are exposed during their long migrations, for the Monarch is a true aristocrat and winters in the South.

A gold-dotted chrysalis hung suspended where the caterpillar had been

Originally it was a tropical butterfly, but owing to numbers its food, probably, became scarce; in consequence of this the more hardy members of the race began to follow the milkweed northward, until to-day these butterflies may be seen in Canada from early summer until fall, when they assemble in flocks for the return migration. Miss Alberta Field, a careful student of birds and butterflies, writes me that she was fortunate enough during the last days of September to witness one of these migrating hosts, when— "thousands of Milkweed butterflies covered the fences, shrubs, and weed tops on a country road. They were like myriads of living blooms, flitting from leaf to leaf, on their way to sunny

I could see the color and markings of its wings

climes, winged gorgeousness whom Nature's instinct guides to sheltering warmth."

They, or more likely their children, make the spring trip singly or in small groups, and I have noticed that the males appear in advance of the females. It is not difficult to distinguish one from the other, as Sir Monarch carries a diminutive sachet of black velvet on each of his hind wings, the perfume of which, no doubt, is distilled for the benefit of his lady-love.

CHAPTER XXIX

SILVER–SPANGLED BUTTERFLIES

THE ARGYNNIS, *Argynnis*

"The gold-barr'd butterflies to and fro
 And over the water-side wandered and wove,
 As heedless and idle as clouds that rove
 And drift by the peaks of perpetual snow."

A "HOPE deferred" was realized when among the litter at the base of a violet plant I found the long-sought spiney caterpillar. During three springs I had searched and searched for the insect upon these plants, especially upon those with irregularly eaten leaves, for it is by such telltale signs that eventually this crawler is located.

At last my efforts were rewarded! In my hand lay a half-grown larva of some one of the beautiful silver-spangled *Argynnis* butterflies—which of them I did not know; it might be *idalia*, *cybele*, or *aphrodite*, but any of these would prove acceptable.

The specimen found had a dark skin with dull orange tubercles; these were tipped with glinting black spines, and together the markings broke the outline of the body so that the caterpillar was practically invisible, for in the background where it rested there were russet stems, shining seeds, and soft damp earth intermingled with the green of growing things.

All of the many species of Argynnis caterpillars are secretive and hard to find, because they feed at night and hide at the base of the plant during the day.

Silver-spangled butterflies

After discovering my larva I could readily understand why the species is so effectually concealed.

If trouble never comes singly, good luck sometimes comes doubly. Ten minutes after finding the first Argynnis I found a second, and went home rejoicing because, at last, I was able to detect these crawlers among the débris which they frequent.

My elation lasted an entire week, then on May tenth one caterpillar died, and three days later forty small larvæ emerged through the skin of the other.

The greater number of these were already encased in tiny silk cocoons when the condition of the Argynnis was discovered. None of the cocoons were attached to the caterpillar, al-

A *cybele* chrysalis

though from bits of thread adhering to its skin an attempt may have been made to place them there.

This crawler, which had been compelled to nourish a brood of parasites, still had enough life within its depleted body to move about for a few hours, then it remained motionless, and I knew that my hope of rearing a silver-spangled butterfly was still deferred.

Another opportunity came early in September, but this time in the form of eggs laid by one of the species, *Argynnis cybele*, which was followed as she flew hither and yon over a field where violets grew. It was a long chase, and many leaves on which she rested were examined before I secured four eggs for my collecting-box. They were of a honey-yellow color, ribbed, and shaped like an old-fashioned sugar-loaf; in time they hatched into rough, warty, greenish-brown caterpillars.

Butterflies of *Argynnis cybele*. A, female; B, male; C, under surface of butterfly's wings

Argynnis larvæ are said to hibernate without feeding; after a few days I found that those of *cybele* were living up to their family reputation, so removed them to a violet plant in the yard. But the following spring the leaves were not eaten, which was an indication that the little crawlers had died during the winter.

I had learned how to spy out these caterpillars, however, and secured mature larvæ in June, one of which pupated on the twenty-second of the month. At first the wing covers of the chrysalis showed an old-rose color and the body section markings of dull yellow. The following day the surface of the pupa darkened, but to the end it retained a rosy tinge.

On July seventh the butterfly pushed up the trap-door covering its face and stepped forth; its wings were tawny yellow marked with black, and on the under surface of the hind wings I caught the glint of what Mrs. Comstock so aptly calls butterfly money—"silver dollars and half-dollars" in plenty.

Why the mothers of this race of airy butterflies delay their work of egg-laying until early fall is beyond human ken, but it is one of the peculiarities of *Argynnis*. They fly for several weeks before they oviposit. As a result, the little caterpillars when they hatch seem to realize that the season is so far spent that they cannot hope for a sufficiency of food to carry them to the chrysalis period; so they snuggle down among the violet stems, without even a bite, and there they sleep during the winter. But when spring calls they are quite ready to feast upon the young leaves which the plant offers.

CHAPTER XXX

THE LITTLE BLUE BUTTERFLY

THE SPRING AZURE, *Cyaniris pseudargiolus*

"Or is thy lustre drawn from heavenly hues,
A sumptuous drifting fragment of the sky."

THERE is a dainty little blue butterfly that appears early in the spring. Professor Comstock says that in localities where it occurs it is the first butterfly of the season, excepting, of course, such species as hibernate in the adult form.

It is commonly called the Spring Azure, and the name seems more appropriate to me than the longer scientific one of *Cyaniris ladon violacea*, so I am going to use it.

The small creature is polymorphic, that is, it appears in several different forms, and this change of dress has been the subject of careful study by such lepidopterists as were William H. Edwards and Samuel Scudder.

These differing forms of the butterfly appear one after the other as the season advances, and a special name has been given to each.

The late spring and summer forms are thought to be the

same by Dr. Scudder, who calls these varieties *Cyaniris pseudargiolus,* a name more difficult to remember than that of
the first brood. So let us be content to know this butterfly as
the Azure or the "Little Blue."

I had heard that the early butterflies of this species lay their
eggs in the flower clusters of the Dogwood, while those of the
next generation lay them on Black Cohosh, *Cimicifuga race-*

The Little Blue butterflies

mosa. Season after season, I searched these plants for the
larvæ, but the search had always ended in disappointment until the tenth of last July. Then in a wood where Black Cohosh
grows profusely, I found its tall flower spikes white with buds.
Of course I stopped to examine them. The first plant yielded
me six caterpillars, and I soon found that I could gather a hundred of the larvæ if so inclined. They were of all ages and
conditions—some but recently emerged from their shells, and
others with rosy skins, which indicated that they were nearing
the pupa state.

Photograph by Bash

Caterpillars on buds of black cohosh

I did not find any eggs, but there were plenty of empty shells, usually on the bud or bud stem, each turban-shaped with a hole in the top through which glimmered the "silver" lining. The outer surface of these tiny shells under the lens showed a tracery of lace work that was very beautiful.

The caterpillars were slug-shaped, and as they adhered closely to the stem or to the buds on which they fed, it was difficult to detect either feet or pro-legs. The largest speci-mens were one-third of an inch in length, and this measurement was exclu-sive of the neck, which, being extensile like that of the turtle, could thrust the head well forward or con-tract so that both neck and head were concealed by the thorax.

The head, small and shiny black, was rarely visible, however, for the larvæ of this Little Blue has a nice taste in flower food and eats only the stamens and ovules.

198

These it secures by pushing its head and long neck through a round hole which it cuts in the side of the bud.

One friend of the butterflies offers an excuse for such vandalism by suggesting that the insect in devouring the heart of the flower assists Nature in her annual pruning.

I did not notice the caterpillars on opened blossoms, but I found that in confinement they eat into the small greenish buds after the older ones have been ravished. Then one day when the food had given out entirely I caught a fully grown individual deliberately devouring one of its companions that was so near the chrysalis period it could offer practically no defence.

I removed the cannibalistic crawler and its victim to a glass vial in which I had placed a short stem of fresh buds. I did this in order to learn whether a caterpillar that has once tasted animal food will, from preference, continue the diet when its natural plant food is procurable. In this case the larva resumed its vegetarian habits. I am not certain, however, but that it did so simply because it came in contact with the fresh buds before it located the body of its murdered relative. The Little Blue is not the only caterpillar that dines upon its brothers and sisters if occasion demands self-preservation; in fact, it is a characteristic of several members of the family *Lycænidæ*.

As the head of this caterpillar is so constantly hidden within the treasure-chests of the plant, the insect cannot readily defend itself against the parasitic flies which endeavor to lay their eggs upon its body, so it has the semblance of another head painted on the first thoracic segment, and this brown mark, no doubt, causes more than one wee creature to hesitate when preparing to alight upon the oval back of the larva.

There are some peculiar organs at the caudal end of this crawler which also aid incidentally in protecting it from enemies. One of these organs is located near the middle of the tenth segment, and with a lens we can see the slit through which the tube is evaginated and sometimes even the tube itself, with a wee drop of green liquid on its tip. Below this organ, on the eleventh segment, are a pair of minute spots that indicate the position of other tubes.

As ants are always found upon the flower-stalks of Black Cohosh when these larvæ are present, the behavior of the two insects has been studied in reference to each other, and it has been ascertained that the ants drink the green liquid, and, in some cases at least, defend the caterpillars which furnish the treat.

The use of the organs on the eleventh segment is not definitely known, but they probably signal when the feast is ready, possibly by emitting an odor through the tentacles that encircle their tips. I have seen these tubes emerge and work in and out rapidly at the approach of an ant, which invariably began to caress the caterpillar with its antennæ. In response the green liquid would be offered and eagerly drunk.

The color and markings of the Little Blue larvæ vary greatly, but whether their skins are white, greenish-yellow, or covered by a geometrical pattern like an old-fashioned quilt, there is always a dark spot on the ninth segment directly above the honey-tube opening. The spot cannot help the ant in finding the liquid, however, for her poor sight would make it impossible for her to see the signal.

These larvæ are so like the flower-buds in color that one might easily overlook them were it not for the presence of the ants and the telltale round openings in the buds. They are ravenous little crawlers, and the heart of many a blossom is required to satisfy the appetite of each before it reaches its chrysalis period, the coming of which is always indicated by a rosy tinge in the skin.

When ready to pupate a caterpillar weaves a flimsy mat of silk on a support and passes a loop about its body which it attaches to this web, but the work is so poorly done that the slightest touch loosens the insect unless it is suspended among the buds, in which case the chance of disaster is somewhat lessened because the bud stems act as braces.

Later the maturing seed-balls protect the pupæ in another way, for while each chrysalis is white or greenish-white when it emerges, it gradually assumes the brown tones of the withering buds and of the follicles, and among these it remains an inconspicuous object.

Photograph by Bash

Larva with geometrical pattern, and bud showing opening through which it has fed

More than one of my captured caterpillars failed to pupate because of the parasitic larva that was developed within its body. A tiny black speck upon the skin indicated a stung specimen, from which in due time a white maggot would always appear and soon after change to a small brown puparium, the cradle of the future fly.

I found the first chrysalis of the Azure butterfly on July twelfth, and from that date until the twenty-seventh of the month they continued to form. Then my only remaining caterpillar cast its skin for the last time, and I waited for the birth of the butterflies.

One emerged on July twenty-ninth. With wings spread it measured one and one-fourth inches—truly, a large insect to have come from so small a chrysalis. As it flew to a sunny window the heavy black margins on the tips of the blue fore wings designated it as a female. The hind wings were not of so blue a color, but the entire upper surface of the butterfly as well as the nearly white under surface had an iridescent glimmer like that of certain polished seashells. The butterfly was quick in its movements and seemed to be forever sensing out things with its delicate black-and-white banded antennæ.

Photograph by Bash

Chrysalides of Little Blue butterfly

The males when they arrived lacked the heavy dark margins, but the under surface of their wings was ornamented like those of the female with rows of irregular black spots.

The size and depth of color of these spots vary with the seasonal form of the butterfly, and therefore assist in the identification of a specimen.

The early arrivals, however, are never so large nor so heavily margined as this summer brood, but in West Virginia and from there southward the Spring Azure shows another peculiar form, that of a brownish-black male.

All Southern males do not affect this dark coloring, however, as many appear in the characteristic blue of the species. But in whatever form the insect comes it is welcome, for, as Mrs. Comstock says, "The more incarnations of so beautiful a butterfly the better."

CHAPTER XXXI

"RAG CARPET" WORMS

THE BLACK SWALLOW-TAIL, *Papilio asterias*

"Some to the sun their insect wings unfold."

ONE afternoon in August Maggie came to the house carrying a discarded fruit can, a sure sign that she had brought something of interest to me. The can on this particular day held about a dozen caterpillars measuring from one-eighth to two inches in length. They were variously marked, the smallest being black with two rows of dull orange warts and saddle-cloths of pale yellow, while others, "a little older grown," retained the saddle-cloths but had bright yellow spots in place of the dull orange. These also showed faint bands of white and yellow. The white became green in the largest of the "worms," and on the black portions between these bands the yellow was evenly distributed in the form of small disks.

That summer I was studying birds and had become interested in caterpillars largely because they served as food for certain varieties I knew absolutely nothing of insects, and at the small library in the town I could gain butlittleinformationon the subject. So I was obliged to learn what I could from obser- vation, and it was an experience big with pleasant surprises and sore disappointments.

Maggie, the dearest of girl neighbors, was a willing assistant in my investigations and ever on theoutlookforspeci-

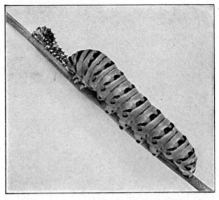

" Rag carpet " worms

mens. Some time before she had told me about caterpillars that fed in her garden on the leaves of parsley, dill, turnip, etc., and said that they looked like bits of rag carpet, so when I uncovered the can I at once recognized its inmates as the "rag carpet" worms of her description.

As she poked one with a bit of twig, it shot forth from its head a reddish V-shaped prong which emitted a most sicken-

A partly grown caterpillar

ing odor. We discovered that each and every one of the caterpil- lars had a sim- ilar organ, and that it was not loath to use the same upon the slightest prov- ocation.

When I returned to the city I learned that this pliable double horn is called an osmaterium. The added information that its use is for defence was for me superfluous. I had found this out for myself and more— Shall I tell you what? In so doing I may steal the caterpillar's thunder, but really there is no need for his wormship to be so constantly on the defensive and offensive with its ill-smelling prong. It is perfectly harmless. There, the secret is out.

These caterpillars of the Black Swallow-tail butterfly, *Papilio asterias*, are probably better known than any of the other larvæ of the Swallow-tail group, for they feed upon so many common plants in our gardens, like carrots, caraway, dill, parsnip, and parsley, that a very little experience in gardening is certain to bring the gardener in contact with them, and such contact is usually the undoing of the "worms." But those which Maggie had captured were not to be sacrificed. Instead, they were watched and tended daily by a woman who at the time had never owned a garden.

I speculated a good deal over the colors and markings of this family before I understood in the least why they differed in appearance, then one day, to my astonishment, a half-grown individual wiggled head first through its splitting skin and stood apparelled in the gorgeous green, yellow, and black of a mature "rag carpet" worm. It was another first experience, and, therefore, an experience to be remembered.

One evening I discovered that the caterpillars had eaten their food down to the very last bite. The absence of leaves enabled me to see that a large, faded specimen had spread a silken mat upon the side of the jar and was clinging to this with its prolegs. Being a Swallow-tail larva it held its body erect, and I noticed that it was spinning silken threads and twisting them into a loop, which presently it adjusted about its body.

Then in this "swing," it settled down to wait for its transformation.

But every one of its companions seemed to take a fiendish delight in annoying it, and being at the time very ignorant of insects, I wondered if such behavior was intentional, accidental, or incidental to the quest for food, for as they crawled over and under each other the large caterpillars would snap at the little ones, which in turn would shoot out their wee scent organs and wave them in the most impudent "touch-me-if-you-dare" manner. The war was still being waged when I went in to supper, and as soon as the meal was finished, I hastened to Maggie's garden for parsley. It was dark when I returned. In the morning I found that in putting the fresh leaves into the jar I had loosened the suspended caterpillar, and as a consequence it had failed to produce a chrysalis. My clumsy fingers in

Photograph by Snyder
Chrysalis (slightly enlarged so as to show attachment)

a second's time had ruined the patient work of hours. I think of the crushed insect with regret even to this day. Its "trouble had all been in vain."

Other chrysalides appeared in rapid succession, however, each supported in the silken loop which the larva had spun before it discarded its last skin; and I found that some chrysalides were of a pea-green color daubed with chrome yellow, and others were in shades of soft brown, while a few of the green ones became brown after a time.

The pupa state averaged ten days. When the butterflies emerged they had black velvety wings crossed by two rows

Black Swallow-tail butterflies

Photograph by King

These butterflies are frequently seen along the roadways

of yellow spots, and there were blue scales upon the hind wings of the females, which distinguished them from the males. These butterflies are frequently seen in our yards and along the roadways where "Queen Anne's lace" is growing. For as this plant is one of the family *Umbelliferæ*, Madam Swallow-tail often selects it as food for her children.

Two of the chrysalides formed by caterpillars from Maggie's garden did not open that fall, but one morning in the following March I found a very small but perfect Black Swallow-tail butterfly upon the window-curtain of the room in which the specimens were kept. For days it flew about the house, and often lit upon a jar of twigs which I had gathered for early blooming. Once it uncoiled its long tongue and tried to sip the nectar from a tulip, later it drank quite a little sweetened water from my fingers, but in my eagerness to be of service, I got the sticky stuff upon its legs and made them stiff. After this the butterfly neither ate nor showed much interest in life.

Before it died, the second Swallow-tail appeared, but I could not induce it to taste the dainties which I offered. Did the first arrival bid it beware of syrup and of me?

CHAPTER XXXII

A CLEVER CATERPILLAR

The Troilus Papilio or Green Cloud Swallow-Tail,
Papilio troilus

> "He who feels contempt
> For any living thing, hath faculties
> Which he has never used—thought with him
> Is in its infancy."

I HAVE a garden filled with weeds, and here I entertain many of my most interesting guests, namely, the butterflies and their children. True, the butterflies usually stop for lunch among the cultivated flowers, for these they find more to their liking. But if the weeds do not feed many of the butterflies they feed the butterflies' children, and that is quite as important, for butterflies are particular as to the food that nourishes their caterpillars. When ready to lay their eggs, they fly miles, if necessary, to find the desired plant on which to oviposit.

Since most species of butterflies lay only one or two eggs on a leaf and but few on a plant, this searching and egg-laying consumes a great deal of time. However, the butterfly does not need to hasten this work as does the silk-moth, whose days are numbered; instead, she flits hither and thither and rarely blunders in her choice of a feeding-place for her young. Only once have I found a butterfly's egg on any but the larva's food plant. This egg was deposited by a Madam Turnus,

Photograph by King

It just touched the blossoms as it passed

and I saw her place it upon a leaf of white syringa. I secured the egg, but when it hatched into a Turnus caterpillar it refused to eat syringa leaves, so I fed it upon tulip-tree leaves until it had passed its second moult, when it escaped.

As I wish to have the butterflies come to my garden, and, coming, find that for which they search, I plant weeds, vines, shrubs, and even trees for their convenience; but the man who cares for the place does not like caterpillars, and when one with an osmaterium thrusts forth its weapon just to show that it does not like the man any better than the man likes it, the man is quite certain to kill the "worm." But he admires the butterflies, and one sunny morning while I sat under the old pear tree

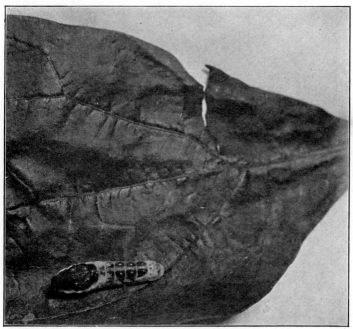

Photograph by Snyder

A partly grown larva

he called my attention to a large dark Swallow-tail flitting among the flowers. It did not drink from the blossoms as it passed, but just touched them, as if to find out what they were like. When the insect came nearer I saw that it had a greenish-blue color on the upper surface of its hind wings, and knew it for *Papilio troilus*, or Green Cloud Swallow-tail. I suspected that

Photograph by Lustig

The Green Cloud larva fully grown, showing leaf-house in which it lives

she was smelling out the young sassafras that I had planted for the convenience of her family, so I picked up my field-glass and kept an eye on her doings. Yes, slowly but surely, she was going toward that part of the garden where the sassafras grew, and all at once she flew straight to the tree and seemed perfectly at home, for she remained very still for several moments, then she stretched her wings and sailed away over the meadow.

I located the leaf on which she had rested and soon found her tiny pale green egg attached to its under surface.

This happened on June thirtieth. I tried to keep a close watch on the egg, but in the end missed seeing the young caterpillar come forth. When I examined the sassafras leaf on the morning of July fifth, there was the odd little olive larva, all humps and bumps and bristles, and so intent upon eating its egg-shell that it would not stop even when prodded with a grass stem. At 8 A. M., however, it had finished the meal, and then it travelled to the upper side of the leaf, where it spun a little silk carpet, on which it rested. Later in the day it crawled to the edge of the leaf and ate out

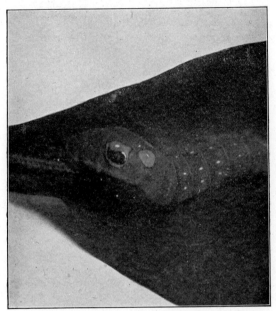

Photograph by Lustig

Its big eye-spots seemed to glare at me most wickedly

a piece the size of a small pin's head, then returned to its carpet with no seeming hesitation.

At 6 P. M. the larva went to the side of the leaf opposite to that on which it had dined, and with its sharp jaws made a short cut in the edge. It then lined this small triangular portion with soft white silk and folding it over onto the leaf, thus secured its first home and hiding-place.

Why should the larva seek concealment? Because it has enemies, such as the mites and the spiders, and in the great plan of Nature the controlling Intelligence gives even to the wee ones their chance to survive and round out their life cycles.

This young Papilio fed at night, usually on leaves some distance from the one on which it lived. It grew so fast that on

July ninth it split its first skin and crawled forth in a new one of brown with light markings on the back. It changed its skin several times before it was fully grown, and also its house, for the first little shelter soon became too small. Every new dwelling was carefully lined with silk, and the last and largest one of all was made by drawing the leaf edges together above the midvein.

Photograph by Lustig
The beautifully proportioned chrysalis emerged

After a meal the larva had no difficulty in locating its home and returned directly to it, showing, it seems to me, that it possessed a faculty akin to memory, for admitting that it retraced its steps by means of a silken pathway spun and spread for the purpose, still it must have been conscious of the fact that at the end of the path a shelter and comparative safety would be found.

When I peeped into this rolled leaf on July eleventh, the Green Cloud, which had become very green indeed, at once hunched up the front of its body so that the big eye-spots on its back seemed to glare at me most wickedly. As I still kept the leaf open it shot out its reddish prong, and, oh! what an odor. But I knew the "worm" was just "bluffing," so I put it, house and all, into a glass jar where I could watch it during the remainder of its creeping days.

A CLEVER BUTTERFLY

By the twentieth of the month the green color of the body had faded to a deep yellow, and on this day the larva attached itself to a sassafras twig with the last silk it would ever spin.

The day following a beautifully proportioned buff chrysalis emerged from the skin of the suspended larva. This in turn yielded, on August eleventh, a perfect male butterfly.

CHAPTER XXXIII

THE PAWPAW BUTTERFLY

THE AJAX OR ZEBRA SWALLOW-TAIL, *Papilio ajax*

"Chasing his lady-love high in the air,
Fluttering gayly,
Frolicking daily,
Free from anxiety, sorrow, and care."

THE "man with the wheel" was closing a contract to place new machinery in a mine, at the mouth of which he and the owner stood. Suddenly he dropped his note-book and, hat in hand, scrambled down the steep bank to the road, where he fell to his knees with the brim of his hat pressed into the dust.

"What in Sam Hill has struck you?" exclaimed the surprised mine-owner. And "the man with the wheel" called back: "Oh, I've caught it all right, but I've broken a bit from one of the wings, so it will not be a perfect specimen. You see," he continued, holding out for inspection a delicate green-and-black Swallow-tail butterfly, "my wife collects and studies these things, and I know she has never had one like this."

While the two men were examining the beautiful creature, another of the same kind flew past them, and the mine-owner said: "This is my try. I'll get the fellow and I'll get him per-

218

fect," which he did. Then when the specimens were chloro-
formed and mailed to me, the business deal was continued.
The next day I received my first *Papilio ajax* butterflies.

Several years later I saw an Ajax flying through the yard of
my new home in Ohio. Was it a native? Yes, for upon in-
quiry I learned that the val-
ley of the little stream that
ran near our place contained
great patches of pawpaw

Photograph by Vignos

Pawpaw "worms"

bushes, the only food plant so
far as I know of the Ajax caterpillars.

It was early in the season in
our latitude for these insects.
Still I went into the valley
hoping to secure at least a few of the crawlers. Possibly I
should have missed them had not the bird lover gone along.
For years he had gathered both the larvæ and their chrysalides—using them in exchange for nests—and knew where and
how to find them. In all we secured seven specimens, but not
until we had searched for a very long time.

It became a regular recreation that summer to go for pawpaw "worms." There was a great fascination in hunting for these odd caterpillars, which we usually discovered on low-growing twigs or on grass stems close to the ground. When not eating a larva would rest with its head drawn back within

the swollen thoracic folds, and it would remain perfectly quiet for long intervals of time but, if disturbed, its offensive osmaterium, transparent like amber, would be thrust out and waved in the usual threatening manner.

The caterpillars feed early in the morning and late in the afternoon when their striped skins make them conspicuous, but when at rest among the lights and shadows of grass and stems these same skins prove a protection.

I never saw a freshly emerged caterpillar that was not of a dull black color with a rough skin; but with the first moult the caterpillars may become quite light

Photograph by Snyder
The chrysalis

or be striped with black. The great variety in the coloring of their coats at different times as well as the difference between individuals of the species was a constant surprise to me.

Some small caterpillars had bands of yellow, black, and white, which they retained until the pupa stage, the coloring becoming more intense with age. Others for a time wore lemon and blue; then lemon, white, and gray; then pale green, or pale green and gray, but in the last stage there was always a heavy mark of

A small Pawpaw butterfly

black and yellow between the third thoracic and the first abdominal segments. Some crawlers turned to chrysalides while in the striped condition, but many took on a very beautiful green before they pupated.

The time seemed long, frequently three days, between the attaching of a larva and the emerging of the chrysalis.

Photograph by King
Summer form of Ajax (two-thirds life size)

The chrysalides were another surprise. The first one was of a deep green, the second of a greenish-brown, the third of a pale pinkish-brown, the fourth green, but light, and the fifth dark brown. The color of a larva, I discovered, had nothing to do with that of its chrysalis.

The butterflies appeared in from fifteen to twenty-four days.

The first came forth with crumpled wings because when the chrysalis shell opened the liquid which it contained made a wet mess at the bottom of the jar, and into this the newly emerged insect managed to flounder until ruined.

There are some variations in the markings of the different broods of the Ajax butterflies. Those from winter chrysalides are smaller, and have shorter tails and less black upon their wings than those of the late spring form, while the butterflies of the summer brood are the largest and darkest of all. The under side of the wings of the Ajax is very beautiful because of an exquisite rose-red band which crosses them. These butterflies have pale green legs and red-brown antennæ.

The females are frequently seen flying from one pawpaw bush to another, intent upon egg-laying, and if you follow one and examine the leaves on which she rests you are quite certain to find her eggs. At first these are of a blue-green color, but this color changes to brown before hatching—a process that requires from six to eight days.

Larvæ reared in captivity do well, and they are not quarrelsome like those of the Black Swallow-tails. They are a clean, wholesome brood upon the fragrant pawpaw branch, and, from start to finish, one of the most interesting families which I have reared.*

* Professor and Mrs. Comstock in "How to Know the Butterflies," tell us that spicebush and upland huckleberry are also food-plants of these caterpillars.

CHAPTER XXXIV

A SOUTHERN SWALLOW-TAIL

THE CRESPHONTES, *Papilio cresphontes*

"Mark, while he moves amid the sunny beam,
O'er his soft wings the varying lustres gleam."

IN the South there are several gorgeous Swallow-tail butterflies whose caterpillars live and thrive upon orange leaves, and one, the Giant Swallow-tail, *Papilio cresphontes*, is especially injurious to these trees.

One morning a box of the larvæ came by mail, with just enough of the food plant remaining to show that it had been prickly ash, *Fagara Americanum*. Naturally I concluded that the specimens would enjoy such "green goods" as their species frequently eat from choice in the open, so begged a few leaves from a neighbor's orange tree, and placed the new-comers upon these in a clean vivarium, certain that they would appreciate the fresh food and spacious quarters after a three days' journey in confinement.

It was the old story with variations, however. The caterpillars at first refused even to taste the leaves, but later, either from hunger or curiosity, they took a few small bites, then crawled away, showing plainly that they were not pleased with my entertainment.

Here was a threatened "Hunger Strike," and I realized that if I were to save the crawlers I must immediately provide the

Photograph by Lustig

The larva that ate orange leaves

food coveted, prickly ash.   But prickly ash is not common in
our locality; in fact, I could not recall having seen a tree, so
I telephoned to the city forester for information.   He replied
that so far as he knew the trees grew in but a single place,
one of the parks six miles from my home and not accessible by
street car.   Fortunately, I have neighbors who are interested

to a degree in my insect nursery. When one of them understood the situation he offered to drive me to the place indicated. I gladly accepted, but within a hundred feet of the park down came a heavy shower, drenching us as well as the grass and trees.

Front view of
chrysalis

I thought of the hungry larvæ, however, and, despite the wetness, I hunted for prickly ash, but to no purpose. We were obliged to return home empty-handed and over roads heavy with mud.

The next day all of the Cresphontes save one died. It, the largest, and, I must say, the wisest, "fell to" after a deal of mincing, and literally gorged itself on orange leaves. Then, like a well-fed snake, it went to sleep and gave us an opportunity to take its photograph.

This caterpillar was startling in appearance. It had an olive-green skin of varying shades, touched here and there with heliotrope and brown. Its thoracic segments were somewhat swollen and appeared to be the head of the insect, largely because a light portion bordering these segments simulated to perfection a big, cavernous mouth, while a pair of small, piercing eye-spots located between the second and third segments strengthened the illusion. But when the insect crawled from place to place, or when it dined, the real head, usually concealed under the sham "mouth," protruded, and there was a face beneath a face.

On July twenty-second this sensible Cresphontes grew quiet. The next day it emptied its intestines and prepared to pass into the pupa state. On the twenty-fourth I found the chrysalis, which seemed small compared with the size of the larva.

It was on this date that I received a second box of caterpillars from my good friend in Vinton, Iowa, and with them

The Giant Swallow-tail butterfly in a moth-like pose

an extra supply of prickly ash leaves, which provisioned the crawlers until I found one of their food trees.

The butterfly from the first chrysalis, a female, emerged on August fourteenth, and when the wings were expanded we induced her to creep upon a vine in the yard.

Much to our disappointment, she showed no inclination to elevate her wings but remained with them extended horizontally; so at the end of two hours we took her picture in this moth-like pose. It gives a good idea of the yellow and black markings of the upper surface, but one must see the insect to appreciate the delicacy of the canary coloring beneath.

I have never secured eggs from this butterfly in confinement, so do not know how they look when deposited. Those received from my Vinton friend, however, were larger than the eggs of any other Swallow-tail studied and had a coating of brownish powder.

Some day I may chance upon a Madam Cresphontes ovipositing, for the insect is spreading northward. Last year I saw two specimens in the open at Ashtabula, Ohio. Why were they there?—because wafer-ash, *Ptelea trifoliata*, grows in abundance at this place, and Cresphontes larvæ are willing to live upon it.

CHAPTER XXXV

THE BLUE SWALLOW-TAIL

The Philenor, *Papilio philenor*

"The butterflies—bright, airy things—"

IF the scientific names of all butterflies were as musical as that of the Blue Swallow-tail, *Papilio philenor*, I am certain we should find it less difficult to become acquainted with the fairy creatures, each of which deserves a title as euphonious as that borne by this fortunate insect.

Although the Blue Swallow-tail lacks the blue color which its common name implies, there is a metallic sheen of greenish-blue upon the velvet of its wings, and this appears to flow back and forth in waves over their black surface whenever the insect moves. The play of color is caused by reflected light from the interwoven blue and black scales that clothe the membrane of the wings, and under a lens these wings appear to be made of tapestry, with a border of light spots on their upper side and brilliant orange markings on the under side carefully stitched in.

"My lady" and her mate are similarly clothed, the only difference being that the border of light spots usually extends onto her fore wings, and the metallic color of these wings is less brilliant than that of the male. Sir Philenor, like Sir Monarch, carries a sachet on each of his hind wings, but it is inconspicuous, being hidden away in a fold of the wing's inner margin.

The expanse of the butterflies is from three to four and one-half inches, and while the insect is not found in any numbers at the extreme north of the United States, it is common about Pittsburg, and from there southward, and again on the Pacific coast.

Professor Comstock reports the Blue Swallow-tail as sometimes wintering in the butterfly state, but for several years I

Photograph by King
The orange markings of the under side (two-thirds life size)

have reared the insects, and my personal experience has been that all passed the cold weather as chrysalides.

Once in February a beautiful butterfly emerged and flew about the house for several days, to the delight of a convalescing child, who fed it sweetened water; but at length it found an open window and passed out into a cold and snowy world.

Under normal conditions the butterflies do not appear until the Dutchman's pipe, *Aristolochia sipho*, and the Virginia snake-root, *A. serpentaria*, put forth their leaves, for it is on these plants that the females lay their eggs. They deposit them close together and attach them with a maternal glue that probably is responsible for the brown color of the shells.

One set of eggs which I secured hatched on July twenty-third.

Photograph by King

My lady and her mate

The little crawlers were of a light mahogany-brown color, very shiny, and with four rows of tubercles that grew smaller toward the caudal end of the body.

These young caterpillars seemed anxious to keep together, for they arranged themselves in rows and ate and rested with bodies touching. When three days old many of them moulted, each upon a small mat of silk. After this first skin was shed a larva was quite different in appearance. Its body no longer

Photograph by Vignos

After the fourth moult

had a shiny surface; instead it was of a dull chocolate-brown, with tubercles more pronounced, those on the first segment being much like horns, while a suggestion of dull yellow showed in the tubercles along the back. The wee crawlers found no difficulty in using their scent organs whenever the spirit moved them, although usually they were quiet and good-natured.

On July thirtieth several cast their skins for the second time, their bodies becoming a rich madder-brown, and the

Photograph by Vignos

The insects went tap-tapping about

dorsal tubercles, excepting the last three pair, assuming an orange color. A patch of this color also appeared on the first segment between the tubercles, that were now much longer than the others, with tips curved up and in like the horns of a cow.

The caterpillars were great feeders and consumed an enormous quantity of leaves. In fact, my inroads upon a neighbor's Pipe-vine, in their behalf, became so frequent that the owner decided I was injuring the plant, so refused to give me more of the leaves. As a consequence of this refusal I was obliged to make long journeys to a remote part of the town in order to secure provision for the larvæ during the last stage of their creeping existence.

The third moult began on August third, and the caterpillars reappeared in madder-brown skins, but the orange tubercles had become red, while those on the tenth, eleventh, and twelfth segments were somewhat elongated and those of the thorax decidedly so. The larvæ were rather uncanny after this moult, for they looked as if the slightest touch would cause their bodies to become a black, slimy mess.

After the fourth moult, on August seventh, the skins grew to be a dark velvety brown, and the horns on the first segment had the color of red wine. These grew to be a half-inch in length, very tapering and flexible, and the insects went tap-tapping about with them, just as a blind man goes with his cane.

The caterpillars developed rapidly and had become some three inches in length, when on August fifteenth I found one preparing to pupate. It had expelled the liquids from its body, but, even so, I saw it eat a little from a leaf as if it was not quite ready to relinquish its larval state. Soon after this last meal, however, it attached itself to a twig in the usual Swallowtail manner. Its body contracted, and it had a ridiculously huddled appearance with its long tubercles hanging limp and useless at the sides.

On the seventeenth I found the chrysalis, but its support had been insufficient, and the pupa lay injured and dying on the bottom of the breeding-cage.

By August twenty-second all of the caterpillars had turned to chrysalides, and I put them away, believing that the butterflies would not appear until the following year. But they began to emerge on September seventh. The resurrection of these insects was not timely, so they were sacrificed and used as mounted specimens, but had I owned a Pipe-vine I am quite certain that I could have carried a third brood of Philenor caterpillars into their pupa state.

S. Louise Patteson

Chrysalides (three-fourths life size)

CHAPTER XXXVI

AN UNEXPECTED GUEST

THE TURNUS, *Papilio turnus*

"A golden butterfly, upon whose wings
There must be surely character'd strange things."

A TULIP tree grew in the yard of our new home, and soon after we took possession of the place, the little invalid mother and I watched with interest the unfolding of the odd-shaped leaves. These had been tucked away within the brown winter buds so that each occupied a minimum of space. Later, when the flowers appeared, great greenish-yellow blossoms, the little invalid spent much of her time under the tree, for its beauty was a delight to us both, and the warm spring days made out-of-doors doubly dear because of the long months in the sick-room.

During May we noticed bright straw-color and black butter-flies with long tails about the tree, attracted, as we then supposed, by the nectar of the flowers; the little mother made the discovery that some of these butterflies had blue scales upon their hind wings, and wondered what the color indicated. An insect-book enlightened us. The blue is the hall-mark of the females of *Papilio turnus*, a butterfly which frequently oviposits upon the leaves of the tulip tree. After we had learned these facts the little woman was very anxious to see the eggs; but although I kept an eye upon these butterfly visitors they seemed

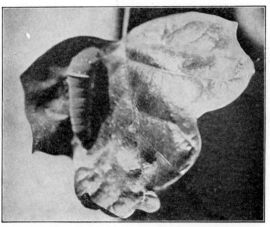

The Turnus, when not feeding, rests upon a mattress
constructed of silk threads

always to alight high among the branches, and it was the first of August before I saw a female settle upon a leaf within reach and remain there for several moments. After her departure I examined the place where she had been, and, to my delight, found a wee green egg. I picked the leaf and placed its stem in a jar of wet sand, then together the little invalid and I rejoiced over our find.

Ten days later we discovered a "bit" of a caterpillar close by the empty shell. It was brown with a white saddle-patch

Photograph by King

A straw-color and black butterfly

on its back. At first we housed the larva in a jelly glass, but this soon became too small a nursery, for the insect grew rapidly and frequently changed its skin, showing, as it did so, startling characteristics.

The Turnus, when not feeding, rests upon a mattress constructed from silk threads spun and attached to the upper side of the leaf, and in such a manner that a space is left beneath the couch, which, as the invalid said, was a wise precaution against damp bedding in wet weather.

We found that our specimen always made a new and larger mattress before moulting, and on this, high and dry, we would later discover it freshly attired.

From the first the V-shaped scent-organ of the crawler was much in evidence, but the little mother never became accustomed to the offensive odor emitted, and insisted that the Turnus was an ill-mannered caterpillar.

Like all caterpillars it was a voracious feeder and ate a great many tulip-tree leaves ere it reached its full length of two and a half inches. Then what a beauty it was! The skin, a soft velvety green, showed a somewhat darker shade over the thorax where the eye-spots were located, and these eye-spots were most

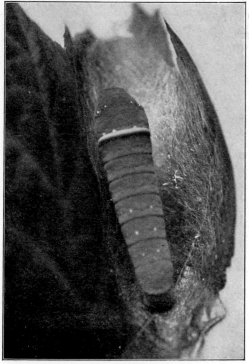

Photograph by Lustig

A full-grown caterpillar

cunningly drawn. In each there was a blue iris outlined in black and surrounded by yellow, with a black dash so placed that it suggested an upper lid. If the Turnus was disturbed, it would distend and rear the front of its body exactly as does the Green Cloud, while the thoracic portion would assume the same snake-like appearance. To one unfamiliar with the insect it became a truly terrifying creature at such times; to us, however, its antics were most amusing.

On September nineteenth this interesting larva attached itself to the side of the breeding-cage, and on the following morning the little mother, the "young entomologist" and myself, with camera focused upon it, awaited develop-

Photographs by King
into the

ments. At 11.10 the insect contracted and expanded its body rapidly. Rip! The skin over the thorax parted. Click, the camera caught the emerging pupa, and thrice

transforming

Suspended caterpillar

again, before it was entirely free from the ruptured skin. Then a fifth click gave us the soft chrysalis suspended where the caterpillar had rested. The next day this chrysalis was firm, perfect in shape, and of an old-wood color, so we photographed it for the second time.

The little invalid, who had watched thus far the development of the insect, was greatly disappointed because the pupa had formed so late in the season that we could not hope for its winged inmate before the following spring. She

the Turnus

chrysalis of

pupa, or

wanted to see the butterfly.

During the winter we went to a distant part of the country, taking with us a number of chrysalides, among them that of the Turnus. As the chrysalides were in an open box in a warm room, I was not surprised on Easter morning, April second, to find a large Swallow-tail butterfly on a hyacinth in the window. At first I supposed, from its dark wings, that it was a common Black Swallow-tail, but soon discovered that I was mistaken, for the yellow and orange marks were differently arranged.

The specimen seemed unfamiliar to me, so I examined the pupæ; that of the Turnus was empty. The newly emerged butterfly was, then, the melanic, or dark female of the species, a dimorphic form which is common only in the warmer sections of our country. By close examination the characteristic

The dark form of *Papilio turnus* butterfly

black bands of the Turnus could be traced in her dusky wings, while on her hind wings were to be seen the blue scales and orange lunules of the ordinary yellow female.

I wheeled the little mother to the window and showed her our "unexpected guest."

She looked up happily and exclaimed: "Why, it is an Easter greeting from Dame Nature"; then, after she had watched the exquisite creature for a few moments, as it fluttered from flower to flower in its search for nectar, she added:

> " ' When we read what is still unread
> In the manuscripts of God,'

we find that Dame Nature is a wonderful old nurse. What a variety of methods she employs in caring for her own!

Photograph by King
The characteristic black bands can be traced in the dusky wings

She paints the wings of the Antiopa so that the butterfly can disappear at will; she makes the Monarch unpalatable, and allows the Viceroy to copy its dress; she furnishes the Little Blue larvæ with a guard of watchful attendants, and the Juglandis with its warning notes; she gives to certain caterpillars a protecting coat of spines, to the Sphinx a harmless but efficient caudal horn, and to the Green-cloud its terrifying eye-spots; but, strangest of all, she compels a portion of the Turnus ladies to wear this sombre garb in order that they the more easily may escape dangers and disasters to which their gayly gowned sisters are always exposed."

"Yes," I replied, "she is a clever and versatile old nurse, ever waiting

> " ' To sing a more wonderful song,
>   Or tell a more wonderful tale '

to those of us who stop and listen."

APPENDIX

The body of the mature caterpillar (*Nymphula Icciusalis*) was fusiform, subcylindrical, slightly depressed, and broadest at the middle. The surface was subopaque, of a pale grayish-yellow color, and seemed to be laid in folds, regularly placed, in which were rows of indentations or pits. As the larva moved the depth of the pits varied. A few stiff setæ extended along the sides of the body, and there were four pairs on the anal shield. The head was rather small, brownish or dull yellow, with two small porrect setæ on its vertex, the Y-mark edged with dark; labrum emarginate; mandibles sharply toothed, and dark; first antennal joint truncate—conic; second, slender, tipped with a seta and three minute articles; ocelli five; hairs and setæ on the head, and the first and second segments as shown in the illustration. The true legs were stout, with dark tips, while the short prolegs had on their lower surface a narrow oval of small dark hooks.

INDEX

247

INDEX

INDEX

6666